Heeres-
geschichtliches
Museum Vienna

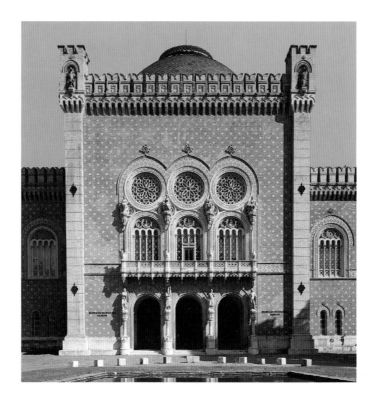

Table of Contents

Author: Manfried Rauchensteiner
with the assistance of Günter Dirrheimer, Claudia Ham, Christoph Hatschek, Brigitte Holl, Ilse Krumpöck, M. Christian Ortner and Walter A. Schwarz

Catalogue designed by Fritz Vesely
Photographs by Manfred Litscher, photo and picture archive of the Museum of Military History

© Verlag Styria
© Heeresgeschichtliches Museum, 2000
Printed by Druckservice Styrian GmbH

ISBN 3-222-12835-9

View of the Imperial and Royal Arms Museum at the Arsenal
RUDOLF VON ALT
Water-colour, 1857

A House of History:
The Museum and its Collections

The year of the revolutions of 1848 is generally regarded as having led to the construction of a building complex in the south-east of Vienna that had a primarily military purpose and was subsequently called the "Arsenal". The military complex erected was supposed to house troops and arms. To this ensemble, however, a prestigious edifice was added that would house the first museum to be built in Vienna. It became clear that the Arsenal was to be more than merely functional; it was, on the contrary, meant to contribute to the royal capital of

the Habsburg Monarchy an architecturally impressive and beautifully composed complex of buildings. The competition was won by two teams of architects: one of them made up of Eduard van der Nüll and August von Siccardsburg, the other one of Ludwig Förster and Theophil Hansen. Förster and Hansen were awarded the contract for building the armoury, which was subsequently named the *Waffenmuseum* (Arms Museum). In 1849, the two architects, having planned the armoury in detail, started construction, but their partnership

did not last long and, ultimately, it was Hansen who prevailed. He drew up plans for a building complex 235 metres in length, made up of transversely jutting out wings and corner towers, and a square, tower-shaped central element topped by a dome. The architectural style he chose was Byzantine, mixed with Gothic elements. The façade of the building was fitted with allegorical sculptures created by Hans Gasser, one of the most distinguished sculptors of the time.
The architectural design of the museum was but the introduc-

sted for over one thousand years. In other words, a concept had been developed.

In this context, the suggestion was made to put up sculptures of Austria's most prominent rulers and military commanders in loosely arranged groupings. It was further suggested to preserve, in frescoes, some of the most significant battles and events in military history for posterity.

In his wall-paintings, Carl Blaas hence implemented a programme covering the spectrum of Austrian history. He had to take into consideration not only the character of the building – an edifice that had become, in a way, a synthesis of work known for its meticulous attention to detail – but also the facts and figures he was given by historians. Art, too, was to contribute to a museum that had been built to illustrate the course of Austria through the ages. It was not until 1872 that the project was finally completed.

When the time came to decide which objects to exhibit in the arms museum at the Arsenal, it soon became obvious that, although a museum had been built, it had not been properly considered what to show. It was both too small and too big at the same time – an edifice representing a concept, without the need to be furnished. Above all, the arms collection of the Imperial court was too voluminous to be shown in the hall that had been designed for it.

The collection hence remained in the Arsenal for but a brief period, and was soon moved to the Museum of Art History at the Ringstrasse, which had

tory chapter to the creative history of the house; many more were still to follow. It had, as it were, sparked off a never-ending story. What the Emperor Francis Joseph was to see when laying the cornerstone to the Arsenal on 8 May, 1856, and Rudolf von Alt was to capture in water-colour, was still far from being finished. A year later, the final details were attached to the façades, although the artistic design of the building's interior was to take another sixteen years to be completed. Meanwhile, the architects and artists responsible for the design of the interior (among

them Carl Rahl, Carl Blaas, and, above all, the museum managers, i.e., the first curators and custodians), at least partially disregarded the original architectural purpose of the building to provide a new home for infantry weapons, as well as for the valuable Imperial arms collection. In doing so, they naturally took up existing traditions. Nevertheless, they also projected a new understanding of temporal and spatial dimensions, as well as a new passion for liberty and national identity, onto the various social and political backgrounds of an Austria, which, even then, had existi-

Stairwell with group of allegorical statues ("Austria") by Johannes BENK, 1869

been completed in the meantime.

The museum on the Arsenal premises, however, was also intended to be used in the future. It was, therefore, necessary to settle the question what kind of museum it should be. The answer was that the museum acquired a collection in which every ethnic group of the Empire was represented.

In the years between 1884 and 1891, an industrious board of trustees managed to accumulate a variety of important objects that were to form the nucleus of a large and magnificent collection. On the occasion of Emperor Francis Joseph's first visit, the museum, then called the *Heeresmuseum* (Army Museum), was officially opened, and the efforts of as many as 35 years to shape a policy for the museum had finally been rewarded, at least for the time being.

In 1914, at the start of the First World War, the museum was shut down, but this did not mean that the collectors' enthusiasm had been dampened. On the contrary, in order to balance the budget of the museum, the efforts to build a comprehensive collection were redoubled.

In 1921, the museum was reopened. While some of the acquisitions had been stored away in new depots, a large variety of objects was exhibited in showrooms. Among the more significant of these was a collection, opened in 1923, of paintings dealing with the First World War. For the first time, a considerable number of paintings was included in the exhibition – paintings that put the emphasis on everyday life in the military and the social circumstances of the war situation instead of showing battle scenes and army leaders, as had been the case in the past. After the *Anschluss* (annexation) of Austria by the German *Reich* in 1938, the chief of army museums in Berlin was put in charge of the *Heeresmuseum*, and as early as 1940 the museum was utilized to stage special exhibitions glorifying campaigns of the Second World War. In 1943, the museum relocated the most valuable objects to cache depots, as did other museums in Vienna. On 10 September, 1944, the *Heeresmuseum* was severely hit by U. S. bombs, and the north-east wing was destroyed. More raids followed, in which additional buildings, mainly depots, were destroyed as well. During the Battle for Vienna in April 1945, the Arsenal grounds were ravaged again.

The losses caused by the war were considerable. The Arsenal as well as the cache depots were heavily damaged, and in the end many places were looted. The rebuilding of the museum was started in 1946. Rather than simply refilling it, however, the design of a historical museum of a more integra-

Imperial and Royal Military Museum, 2nd Hall of Arms, arched wall No. 5, c. 1900

Hall of Fame (detail from the series of frescoes by Carl Blaas)

tive character was initiated. The former *Heeresmuseum* was, therefore, renamed *Heeresgeschichtliches Museum* (Museum of Military History). It was provided with paintings from other state collections, in particular from the Museum of Art History and the Austrian Gallery in the Upper Belvedere, thus enabling it to depict historical developments rather than just single episodes. The building could thus be turned into an art museum of a special kind. A collection of model ships provided by the Technical Museum added the navy as a new field. It consisted of significant objects meant to exemplify maritime history and research. The museum was thus transformed into a cultural museum of the first order – an art museum, a technical museum, and a museum of natural history. The collection exhibited in the main building, which has kept its character as a total work of art up to the present day, portrays about five hundred years of Austrian and European history, and the thousands of original and unique objects shown represent an integral part of the cultural heritage of the world.

Hall of Fame (detail: door-handle based on a design by Theophil Hansen)

Hall of Fame (overall view)

Hall 1 | **From the Thirty Years War to Prince Eugene of Savoy**
The Emergence of a Major Power

The first sections of the museum deal with 16th and 17th century Europe. Time and again the struggle for power, territory, and influence ended in armed conflicts. In most of these conflicts, the Holy Roman Empire of the German Nation played a major part. Its centre eventually shifted to Vienna and the Habsburg Monarchy for good. In the beginning, the aim was to retain Imperial authority, which was challenged by the princes of the *Reich* and by its estates; before long, however, matters turned into a fierce struggle among the European powers, ultimately culminating in the Thirty Years War. Changes within the framework of the European powers went hand in hand with the transformation of military affairs and the conduct of war. The equestrian armies of the Middle Ages were a thing of the past. Instead, mercenaries dominated the battlefields. However, procuring money for these armies increasingly became a problem, not least because it was necessary to raise comparatively large armies of up to 100,000 soldiers, which also had to

be equipped with more modern and more expensive weaponry. The triumphant progress of firearms could no longer be prevented. Up until the Thirty Years War, the Imperial armies had been scantily equipped and only for the duration of a single campaign; now they were transformed into a standing mercenary army. Due to the Emperors' persistent financial problems, these huge armies were partly financed by so-called war entrepreneurs, among them Albrecht von Wallenstein, Duke of Friedland. Wallenstein was also one of the most renowned commanders of his time. Like no other commander, he succeeded in leading the Imperial armies to victory. The Thirty Years War, at times considered a religious war, reached a turning point when Wallenstein managed to defeat a Protestant army, commanded by the Swedish king Gustav II Adolph, near Lützen (Saxony) in 1632, the Swedish king being killed in battle. The assassination of Wallenstein in 1634 was meant to restore the Emperor's authority over his troops. This

Generalissimus Albrecht von Wallenstein
LUDWIG SCHNORR VON CAROLSFELD (1788–1853)
Oil on canvas and hardboard, 1823

Prince Eugene of Savoy
JOHANN KUPETZKÝ (1667–1740)
Oil on canvas, between 1717 and 1723

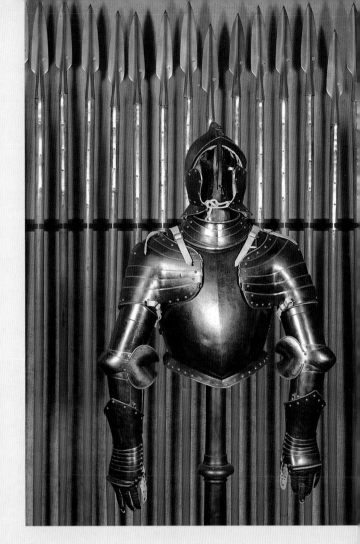

Infantry armour
These armours for infantrymen from the period between 1555 and 1580, consisting of a morion (a high-crested helmet with no visor), breast and back part, a collar as well as arm and leg guards, were worn as protection in close combat. These mercenary infantrymen had largely replaced the aristocratic equestrian armies of the 16th century; known as the so-called *Gewalthaufen,* they formed the core of the army.

goal was accomplished. The war, however, dragged on for another 14 years, until the peace treaties of Münster and Osnabrück in 1648 brought it to an end. During the Thirty Years War, the eastern border of the Habsburg Monarchy remained quiet. In the 16th century the Ottomans had advanced to the west and north; in 1529 they laid siege to Vienna for the first time. For the time being, they had ceased to pose a threat to western Europe. Eastern and southeastern Europe still belonged to the Ottoman Empire, and worries of being invaded remained. It was not until the 1670s, that the Ottomans pushed westwards again. They were organized and armed in a way that was partly different from central European armies. On 1 August, 1664, however, they were defeated by a European army commanded by the Imperial Field Marshal Raimondo Prince Montecuccoli at Mogersdorf near St Gotthard (Szentgotthárd) on the Raab (Rába) river.

Twenty years later, the Ottoman advance reached a crucial stage, when the Turkish army under Grand Vizier Kara Mustapha approached Vienna in July 1683 and laid siege to the city. The relief of Vienna marked a turning point, and the Turkish tide rapidly receded. Under the supreme command of the Polish King John III Sobieski , the Turkish army was defeated by Imperial and Polish troops on 12 September, 1683. Only three years later, Budapest (or Ofen, as the Austrians called it), the capital of Hungary, was liberated after 150 years of Turkish occupation. Belgrade was taken in 1688. In these instances, not only the Margrave Ludwig von Baden, but, more and more, Prince Eugene of Savoy, made their mark as Imperial commanders. The latter, then Supreme Commander of the Imperial troops, defeated the Turks at Zenta (Senta) on the Theiss (Tisza) river in 1679. The Treaty of Carlowitz (Sremski Karlovci, Serbia) put an end to Ottoman domination in the eastern part of Central Europe in 1699. Hungary and Transylvania were incorporated into the Habsburg Monarchy. Austria had become a major power.

Marksmanship drill

Jakob de GHEYN (1565–1629)

Copperplate engravings

Harquebusiers (top) and musketeers (bottom) demonstrate the loading of their weapons. The copperplate engravings can be found in the "Waffenhandlung von Röhren, Musquetten und Spiessen", an instruction manual printed in 1608 in The Hague, teaching the handling of early small arms.

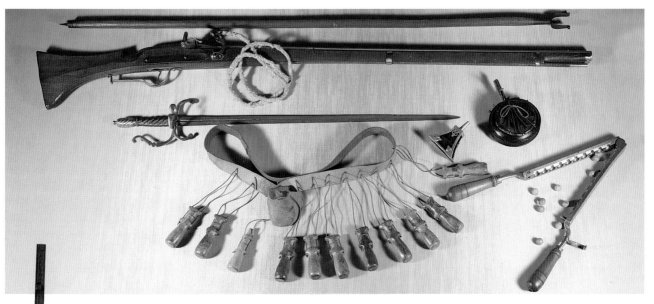

Matchlock musket with accessories

Matchlock muskets were the standard small arms used by musketeers. With a calibre of 18 to 20 mm, the range of the leaden musket balls was 150 to 200 m. The soldiers themselves cast the lead bullets using bullet tongs they carried along. It took an experienced marksman one to three minutes to reload his musket.

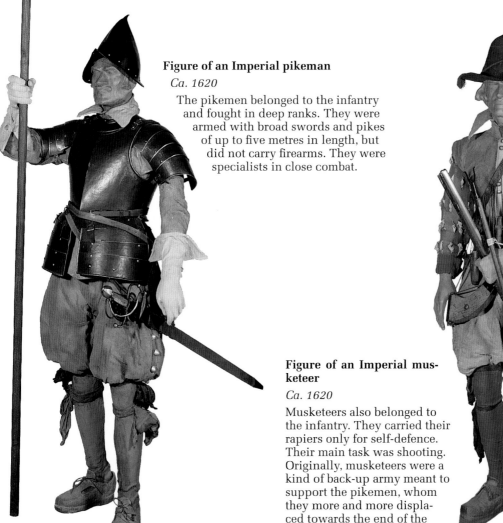

Figure of an Imperial pikeman

Ca. 1620

The pikemen belonged to the infantry and fought in deep ranks. They were armed with broad swords and pikes of up to five metres in length, but did not carry firearms. They were specialists in close combat.

Figure of an Imperial musketeer

Ca. 1620

Musketeers also belonged to the infantry. They carried their rapiers only for self-defence. Their main task was shooting. Originally, musketeers were a kind of back-up army meant to support the pikemen, whom they more and more displaced towards the end of the Thirty Years War.

Frederick V (of the Palatinate; the "Winter King")

Attributed to ADRIAN VAN DER WERFF (1659–1722)

Oil on wood, ca. 1685

Elector Frederick V (1596–1632) was the head of the Protestant Union and accepted the Bohemian royal crown in 1619. After the defeat of the Imperial, Catholic army at the White Mountain near Prague on 8 November, 1620, the king fled to Holland; he had been in power for only one winter.

The Posto near Pressnitz, 27 March, 1641

PEETER SNAYERS (1592[?]–1667)

Oil on canvas

Victorious battle fought by the Imperial and the Bavarian armies under Field Marshal Octavio Piccolomini and the Bavarian *Feldzeugmeister* Baron Mercy against the Swedish troops under Field Marshal Banér near the castle and village of Pressnitz in the *Erzgebirge*.
This painting is one of twelve large-sized battle scene paintings from the time of the Thirty Years War by the Antwerp painter Peeter SNAYERS, ordered by Piccolomini for decorating his castle Nachod in Bohemia.

Generalissimus Albrecht Wallenstein

ANTON BŘENEK (1848–1908)

Bronze, 1882

Generalissimus Albrecht Wenzel Eusebius Wallenstein, Duke of Friedland (1583–1634), was one of the most important Imperial commanders of the Thirty Years War. As a "war entrepreneur" he financed and formed for Emperor Ferdinand II an army which was accompanied by great successes. Suspected of having entered into unauthorized negotiations with the enemy, he was declared an outlaw and assassinated in Eger (Cheb, western Bohemia) in February 1634.

Gustav II Adolph in the Battle of Lützen on 16 November, 1632

PIETER MEULENER (1602–1654)

Oil on oak

The painter, who was born in Antwerp, depicts the crucial scene in which the Swedish king Gustav II Adolph (with blue field sash on a white horse) was fatally hit by a bullet fired by an Imperial cuirassier.

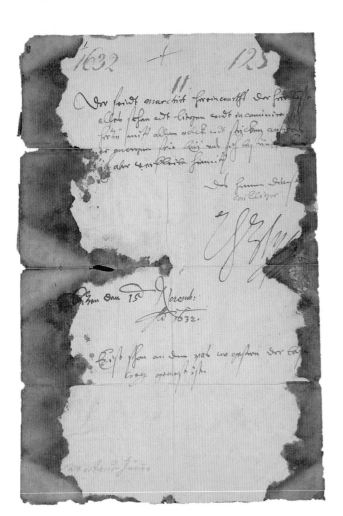

Wallenstein's holograph order to Field Marshal Count Gottfried Heinrich von Pappenheim, Lützen
15 November, 1632

The Imperial *Generalissimus* Wallenstein sent for Field Marshal Pappenheim, who had been ordered to Halle with his unit, one day before the decisive battle against the Swedish troops led by Gustav II Adolph. Pappenheim immediately set off and was fatally wounded in the Battle of Lützen (Saxony) the next day. On the letter one can clearly see traces of Pappenheim's blood.

Assassination of Wallenstein in Eger (Cheb) on
25 February, 1634

Anonymous

Gouache on paper

In this painting Wallenstein's end is depicted by an unidentified German artist at the beginning of the 19th century. The persons involved – Wallenstein in the centre (A), captain Walfer (B) on the left, and captain Dionisius MacDaniel (C) on the right – are identified on an explanatory sheet of paper that accompanies the painting. In reality, however, the deed was by Captain Deveroux in the house of the Mayor of Eger (Cheb).

Emperor Ferdinand III

Jonas SUYDERHOFF (1686) after P. SOUDTMAN

Etching

After Wallenstein's death, Archduke Ferdinand (the future Emperor Ferdinand III, 1608–1657) commanded the Imperial army. During his reign, the peace treaties of Münster and Osnabrück were signed in 1648.

Field cuirass of Count John Sporck

Count John Sporck (1601–1679) distinguished himself as a general of the cavalry in the final phase of the Thirty Years War, particularly in the battle against the Turks at St Gotthard (Szentgotthárd, western Hungary) on the Raab (Rába) river in 1664. The equestrian armour he wears was made around 1630/40 and is regarded as an outstanding example of 17th century German platers' artisanship.

Horses' tails

Tails of differently coloured horsehair mounted on decorated poles. These were emblems of stations whose number demonstrated the rank and distinction of the commander. In the Ottoman army camps there were seven of them in front of the Sultan's, and five in front of the Grand Vizier's tent.

Compound bows and quivers; stirrup

In contrast to European armies of the 16th and 17th centuries, Turkish armies of the time still used bows and arrows. The compound bow was, apart from artillery, the most important long-distance weapon. And it proved superior to the muskets of the time with regard to rate of fire – 10 to 15 rounds per minute – and range – 300 m.

Janissary

ANONYMOUS (From: Abraham a Sancta Clara, Neu eröffnete Welt Galerie [Newly Opened World Gallery], ed. Christoph Weigel, Nuremberg 1703, table 84)

Copperplate engraving

Formed in 1329 by Sultan Orchan, the janissaries were soldiers of the elite corps of the Ottoman army. They numbered approximately 100,000 men.

Turkish colour *(sandjak)*

Red and green silk, ca. 1683

The centre field of this Ottoman standard captured in 1683 outside Vienna contains the key statement of the Islamic creed: "There is no god but Allah, and Muhammad is his prophet". The border braiding displays verses 1 and 6 of the 48th sura of the Koran, the so-called "Victory Sura".

Feather case

This feather case is made of silver and still shows traces of gilt. Its length is 290 mm. It is remarkable for the delicate chasing decorating its surface.
Originally, it was part of the headgear of a janissary officer and accommodated the heron feathers decorating those hats.

Coat of chain mail of Raimondo Prince Montecuccoli

This expensively made coat of chain mail probably belonged to a high-ranking Ottoman dignitary. It stems from Field Marshal Montecuccoli's estate and was seized in the Turkish war of 1663/64. Montecuccoli was the Supreme Commander of the victorious Christian army in the Battle of St Gotthard (Szentgotthárd) on the Raab (Rába) river in 1664. He was later named president of the Court Council of War.

Silver Turkish calendar watch

Southern Germany, mid-17th century

The names of the master craftsmen, Waniek and Raabe, are to be found on the back of the watch. The beautifully decorated face shows, in Arabic characters, the hours, days of the month, and moon's phases; the grooves contain the names of the months and the days of the week as well as, in the Turkish calendar, 1 August, 1664, the day of the Battle of St Gotthard (Szentgotthárd) when it was captured by the Imperial troops.

Seal of the Turkish Sultan Mustapha II

Prince Eugene of Savoy defeated the Turkish army near Zenta (Senta) on the Theiss (Tisza) river in 1697 and captured, among other objects, the seal of the Turkish Sultan. It displays, on its surface, the *thughra*, the entwined lettering and monogram of the Sultan: "Mustapha, son of Muhammad Chan, ever victorious". Below the *thughra* there is the number 1106 of the Islamic calendar, the year of the enthronement of the Sultan, 1695 AD.

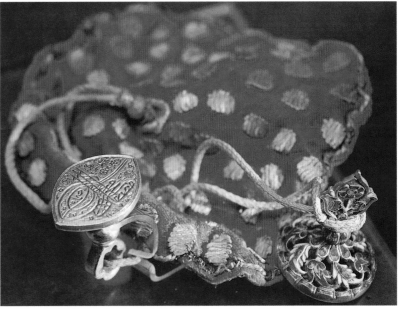

Siege and relief of the city of Vienna in 1683

ANONYMOUS

Oil on canvas, before 1689

The painting, showing the fortified city of Vienna with its siege trenches in the area of Vienna's 7th district and the Turkish camp, combines two episodes: the last mine detonations and the final infantry assault on the Löwel Bastion on 6 September, and the battle of relief on 12 September. The relief army moving down from the Kahlenberg mountain is led by the Polish King John III Sobieski (in the foreground). The Turks precipitously leave their positions.

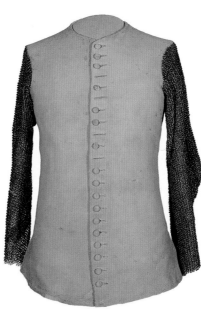

Items of clothing of Prince Eugene of Savoy

The cape collar is a coat-like garment made from goatskin with a narrow stand-up collar; it is preserved only in fragmentary form. The camisole, a waistcoat of yellowish cloth, was worn under the cuirass. The so-called "mail sleeves" were probably attached to it at a later time.

Both garments show how small and frail the prince was.

Prince Eugene of Savoy

Johann Gottfried AUERBACH (1697–1753)

Oil on canvas

Prince Eugene of Savoy (1663–1736) entered the Imperial service in 1683. In 1697, he was made Supreme Commander of the Imperial army in Hungary, in 1701 in Italy, and President of the Court Council of War in 1703. At Zenta (Senta), he achieved a glorious victory over the Turks in 1697. In the War of the Spanish Succession (1701–1714) he was victorious in conjunction with the Duke of Marlborough; and from the Turkish wars of 1716–1718 he also emerged victorious. He also acquired significance as a diplomat, patron of the arts, bibliophile, and castle-owner. – The inscription was attached after 1736.

Officer's sword, commander's baton and cuirass of Prince Eugene of Savoy

The cuirass, consisting of breast and back part, is lined with velvet; the iron rivets and the belt buckle are plated with gold. The breast plate shows the typical proof-marks of the time.
The commander's baton consisting of narwhal horn is equipped with optical lenses on the inside and can thus be used as a telescope.

Funeral pall of Prince Eugene of Savoy (detail)

Black silk velvet with cross inset of gold brocade. Coat of arms of the House of Savoy in relief-like embroidery, 1736

The pall and the wall hanging which goes with it were employed at the prince's funeral honours in Vienna. The little flags on both sides of the respective coats of arms display the places and years of his most important military successes. The gratitude of the House of Habsburg was conspicuous in the way he was given a funeral appropriate to his rank and importance.

Emperor Leopold I

ANONYMOUS

Oil on canvas, ca. 1700

Leopold I (1640–1705), the second son of Emperor Ferdinand III, was crowned Holy Roman Emperor in 1658. Although art and peace loving himself, Leopold had to conduct numerous wars during his long-lasting reign.

Emperor Joseph I

ANONYMOUS

Oil on canvas in the grisaille manner, ca. 1700

Joseph I (1678–1711), the oldest son of Emperor Leopold I, was crowned Holy Roman Emperor in 1690. Thanks to the talent of Prince Eugene of Savoy as commander, he continued the War of the Spanish Succession victoriously. Joseph's early death was a severe blow to Austria's position of power in Europe. It caused the Habsburgs the loss of the Spanish dominions.

Emperor Charles VI

ANONYMOUS

Oil on canvas, ca. 1720

Charles (1685–1740) was born the younger son of Emperor Leopold I. In 1703, after the extinction of the Spanish line of the Habsburgs, he was proclaimed King of Spain (Charles III). However, he did not succeed in defending land and crown in the War of the Spanish Succession (1701–1714). He became Holy Roman Emperor (Charles VI) in 1711.

Colour of the dragoon regiment "Eugene Prince of Savoy"

Red silk, after 1711

On the front there are the entwined initials of Emperor Charles VI, "CRI" (Carolus Romanorum Imperator), beside them, in gold embroidery the reversed initials "EVS" (Eugene of Savoy) of the proprietor of the regiment.

Glass hand-grenades and peak for grenadier's headgear

Around 1700 the grenadiers came into being as a special division of the Imperial infantry. Their main task was to throw hand-grenades filled with black powder that were detonated by a fuse. Grenadiers were employed in pitched battle in critical points or for the storming of fortifications.

Reconstruction of a Turkish audience tent *(otâgh)*

Bell-tent, 7.5 m in height

With their colourful silk-stitched ornaments of Moorish columns and plant motifs, those parts of the tent which have been preserved give an impression of the original magnificence of this prestigious tent owned by the Turkish Grand Vizier Damad Ali who fell in the Battle of Peterwardein (Petrovaradin) against Prince Eugene on 5 August, 1716.

Ten-pound standing mortar

1714

This mortar cast by Leopold Halil in Vienna in 1717 was part of the artillery employed in the siege of Belgrade by Prince Eugene. On 14 August, 1717, the mortar hit the powder-magazine of this Turkish fortress with a bomb. An entire section of the town was destroyed. The inscription, engraved years later, refers to this event.

Hall 2 | Hall of Maria Theresa

The 18ᵗʰ Century

The conflict with the Turks was almost immediately followed by the War of the Spanish Succession (1701–1714). During this war, Prince Eugene commanded the Imperial troops in Southern Germany, Italy, and in the Netherlands. Following this, he went to another war with the Turks, which culminated in the victories of Peterwardein (Petrovaradin, 1716) and Belgrade (1717) and reached its conclusion in the Peace of Passarowitz (Poscharewatz, Pozarevac, 1718). The Habsburg Monarchy thus more and more became a major power in central and south-eastern Europe. And it was Prince Eugene for the most part to whom Austria owed this position.

Shortly after having emerged as a major power, the existence of the Habsburg Empire seemed to be threatened again. For a time, the memory of the victories over the Turks prevailed, particularly the taking of Belgrade. However, another Turkish war fought in coalition with an ever stronger Russia

between 1737 and 1739 caused Emperor Charles VI the loss of most of the acquisitions of 1718. Through the "Pragmatic Sanction" the Emperor tried to secure the inheritance of the Habsburg dominions for his daughter Maria Theresa (1717–1780), but his attempt failed. After the death of her father, Maria Theresa, who was married to Francis Stephen of Lorraine, had to defend her dominions from nearly all her neighbours in the so-called War of the Austrian Succession. At the head of her opponents stood King Frederick II of Prussia, to whom she finally had to relinquish Silesia.

The reforms Maria Theresa subsequently enacted were intended not only to effect modernization, but also to win back the territory that had been lost.

Therefore, her particular attention focused on the army. The monarch was lucky to have at her disposal not only good commanders such as Khevenhüller, Daun, and Laudon, but also organizational

Emperor Francis I Stephen
MARTIN VAN MEYTENS (1695–1770)
(School)

Oil on canvas, ca. 1745

Maria Theresa
MARTIN VAN MEYTENS (1695–1770)
(School)

Oil on canvas, ca. 1745

**Grand Cross and embroidered chest star of the Military Order
of Maria Theresa**

*Golden cross with white enamel on a red-white-red sash, and an embroidered
chest star to go with it*

These decorations were bestowed upon Field Marshal Baron Gideon Ernst
Laudon (1717–1790) in 1758. The Military Order of Maria Theresa was
established in 1757. It was the highest military decoration of the Habsburg
Monarchy.

talents such as Lacy. In the Seven Years War
(1756–1763) they successfully consolidated the
Habsburg Monarchy. They failed to win back Silesia, however.

In the four decades of Maria Theresa's reign
(1740–1780), the appearance of the Austrian army
changed to a more national character. The
establishment of the Maria Theresan Military
Academy in Wiener Neustadt in 1752 was to
improve the training of officers. Homes for invalids
and assistance for the elderly were to be the
incentives for joining an army that still recruited
mercenary soldiers. Besides that, conscription, a
preliminary stage of compulsory military service,
was started in some parts of the country, especially in the so-called "hereditary lands" of the Habsburg Monarchy. Even more significant was the fact
that endeavours to improve the reputation of soldiers in general, and of officers in particular, were
successful. The latter could be made peers for com-

petence or bravery. A particular contribution to
this was the establishment of the Military Order of
Maria Theresa after the victorious Battle of Kolin
(Bohemia) in 1757.

Maria Theresa's son, Emperor Joseph II (1741–
1790), continued with these reforms, while co-
regent (1765–1780) and after he had become
Emperor (1780–1790). The Emperor himself
frequently showed up in uniform; and he was very
open-minded and receptive to the technical innovations of his time. However, his endeavours to im-
pose centralist rule upon the Habsburg Monarchy,
to unify and standardize its administration, and to
counteract the linguistic diversity of all his dominions from Belgium to Hungary, Galicia, and the
Bukovina, met with increasing resistance. Having
failed to consolidate his reforms, he was confron-
ted by rebellions in his dominions and with war.
Once again the Habsburg Monarchy was threatened with disintegration.

Austrian infantry colour, model of 1743

This flag, typical of the early years of Maria Theresa's reign, displays a flame-shaped edging in the colours of Hungary. On both sides of it one can see the Royal coat of arms bearing the arms of Hungary, Bohemia, Burgundy, and the Tyrol together with the Austrian armorial bearings. The coat of arms is flanked by the initials "MT" (Maria Theresa) and "FC" *(Franciscus Coregens)*.

Chair with the initials of Tsarina Elizabeth

Russian armoury of Tula

Folding chair made of steel. Its high-quality surface is remarkable for its artistic brilliance. Back parts and side panels bear brass sheets fashioned with ornaments.

Repeating air rifle, model of 1779, *Girandoni* System, and carbine, model of 1770, *Crespi* System

The Girandoni repeating air rifle (top) was introduced by Emperor Joseph II as a special weapon for hunters and marksmen. The Crespi carbine built for the Austrian cavalry (below) was the first breech-loading firearm introduced by the Imperial and Royal Army.

Pandour captain from Croatia

MARTIN ENGELBRECHT (1684–1756)

Tinted copperplate engraving, ca. 1742

The Pandours were one of a number of Maria Theresa's so-called "subsidiary peoples". As a volunteer corps raised by the Habsburg Army in southern Hungary, they proved best at guerrilla warfare. Among these militias from the military border ranked the Pandour corps of Baron von der Trenck which were subsequently transformed into infantry lines.

Ein Panduren Hauptman aus Croatien, auf eine andere Art.

Grenadier in the Army of Maria Theresa

"Alt Wien" porcelain, ca. 1746

This grenadier belongs to a series of porcelain figures from the Vienna Imperial porcelain factory. They are proof of the respect and popularity the army enjoyed already at the beginning of Maria Theresa's reign. They may have been produced as part of a larger series, presumably ordered by the Imperial house.

Albertina manuscript: Private of the Imperial and Royal Hussar Regiment "Count Hadik"

Gouache on hand-made paper, ca. 1762

The regiment was "lent" to *Generalfeldwachtmeister* Count Andreas Hadik in 1753. It became particularly well-known as a result of its taking Berlin during the Seven Years War.

The manuscript, consisting of 56 of the original 62 sheets, shows by means of 112 figures the ranks of all the arms of the service and of the corps of the Imperial and Royal Army of 1762. This precious manuscript was presumably made for Maria Theresa's son-in-law, Albert von Sachsen-Teschen.

Battle of Kolin on July 18, 1757

August QUERFURT (1696–1761)

Oil on canvas

Maria Theresa called the victory at Kolin the "birthday of the Monarchy". The severe defeat of King Frederick II of Prussia marked a temporary turnaround in the Seven Years War. Frederick was forced to put an end to the siege of Prague, and to withdraw from Bohemia.

Diorama

ANONYMOUS

Ca. 1760

This diorama illustrates the layout of an Imperial encampment by portraying an imaginary evening scene with sutlers, officers' tent, campfire, and army chaplains in front of the troops' quarters.

Field Marshal Count Leopold Daun

ANONYMOUS (MEYTENS School)

Oil on canvas, ca. 1750

Field Marshal Count Leopold Daun (1705–1766) distinguished himself in the War of Austrian Succession (1740–1748) and in the Seven Years War against Prussia (1756–1763). He carried off victories at Kolin (Bohemia) and Hochkirch (Saxony), and forced the Prussian general Finck to capitulate at Maxen (Saxony).

Surprise attack on the Prussian camp near Hochkirch 14 October, 1758

Hyacinth de la PEGNA (1706–1772)

Oil on canvas, 1761

After several failures, the Imperial army under Field Marshal Daun successfully executed a surprise attack on the Prussian army. De la Pegna depicts the incursion of the Austrian troops into the Prussian camp, from which women and their children are fleeing. In this surprise attack about 30,000 men were killed or wounded on the Prussian side.

Headgears for the Prussian infantry from the time of King Frederick II

Mid-18th century

Headgear for grenadiers of the 42nd Fusilier Regiment "Markgraf Heinrich", made of amber cloth, with brass peak in the front. This peak carries a Prussian Royal crown with an inscription below, displaying the motto "Pro Gloria et patria" by Frederick II, and his initials "FR" (Fridericus Rex).

Headgear for fusiliers of the 38th Fusilier Regiment "von Brandes", made of dark-blue cloth with rounded edge on top. Brass peak in the front, similar to that of the grenadiers'.

Spoils from the Seven Years War

Prussian broadswords and bayonets for non-commissioned officers (similar to those of Austrian partisans), captured by Austrian troops between 1756 and 1763.

Colour of the Royal Prussian 17th Field Regiment from the days of King Frederick II

Red field with white corner gussets. In the corners: initials "FR" (Fridericus Rex) with laurel wreath and crown; in the white centre field: black eagle and inscription with motto by Frederick II ("Pro Gloria et patria"); in the middle of each side: a bundle of flames

The flag is a trophy from the Seven Years War. It was probably found among the spoils of war captured in the Battle of Maxen (Saxony) in 1759. Together with the other flags it is one of the rarities of the museum as the stock of the armoury in Berlin was largely destroyed during the Second World War.

Cuirassier on foot and on horseback

JOHANN CHRISTIAN BRAND (1722–1795)

Oil on wood

In these four paintings based on copperplate engravings, the artist depicts the cavalry at the time of Maria Theresa. Jakob Schmutzer's series of soldiers of Maria Theresa's army from 1768 served him as a model. Charming landscapes in the background combine with an exact reproduction of equipment and other paraphernalia.

Field Marshal Laudon riding across the battlefield at Kunersdorf

SIGMUND L'ALLEMAND (1840–1910)

Oil on canvas, 1878

Baron Gideon Ernst von Laudon (1717–1790) was one of the most important generals of Maria Theresa and her son Joseph II. During the Seven Years War he inflicted a crushing defeat on King Frederick II of Prussia on 12 August, 1759, at Kunersdorf (east of Frankfurt). Commissioned by Emperor Francis Joseph I, the picture was painted for the 1878 Paris World Exposition.

Emperor Joseph II in an encampment near Minkendorf

MARTIN FERDINAND QUADAL (1736–1808)

Oil on canvas, 1788

The painting shows Emperor Joseph II with Archduke Francis, later Emperor Francis II (I), and the generals Laudon, Lacy, and Hadik during a "general review", presumably conducted on 27 November, 1786, in the vicinity of the summer residence at Laxenburg castle.

Cadets undergoing balance training

BERNHARD ALBRECHT (1758–1822)

Gouache on paper

The main emphasis of the training at the military academy founded by Maria Theresa was on military matters and sports. The balance exercises on the narrow beams were occasionally made more difficult by having the cadets push wheelbarrows. Bales of straw were supposed to cushion possible falls.

Hall 3 | **Hall of the Revolutions**

From the French Wars until 1848

Towards the end of his reign, Joseph II waged another war against the Turks that again ended with the capture of Belgrade (1789). This victory was more important to Austria than the French Revolution that took place at the same time.

In Paris, on 14 July, 1789, an angry crowd stormed the Bastille, the state penitentiary, a symbol of the much hated rule of King Louis XVI. In April 1792, France declared war upon Austria. The Habsburg Monarchy formed the so-called First Coalition with Prussia and England. The ensuing war lasted until 1797 and ended with the defeat of the allies; for Austria it meant the loss of its dominions in the west of Europe and of Lombardy. It gained Venetia, however. In this war, Napoleon Bonaparte had increasingly distinguished himself as a French general. Austria relied on the military talent of Archduke Charles, the brother of Emperor Francis II, who had achieved a number of victories, including Würzburg in 1796.

In 1799, the Second Coalition War broke out. It was conducted primarily by Austrians and Russians against France. After indecisive fighting in Italy

and Switzerland, Archduke Charles relinquished his command. His brother, Archduke John, who followed him nominally, lost the Battle of Hohenlinden (east of Munich) on 3 December, 1800. The Peace of Lunéville concluded this war. France under Napoleon, who had crowned himself Emperor of the French in 1804, very clearly aimed at dominating Europe. As a consequence, Austria and Russia once again declared war on France in 1805. It ended with the Battle of Austerlitz (Slavkov, southern Bohemia) and the Peace of Pressburg (Bratislava). Austria had to cede the Tyrol to Bavaria which was allied with France. In 1806, Francis II (1768–1853) laid down the crown of the Holy Roman Emperor. He then ruled as Francis I of Austria. In 1809, the Habsburg Monarchy attempted an independent initiative. In spite of the long-lasting conflict with France and its allies, Austria's willingness to make sacrifices seemed undiminished. National enthusiasm steadily increased. Among other things, the establishment of the *Landwehr*, a kind of territorial reserve, was testimony to this. In the campaign, which lasted from April until July,

Napoleon I as King of Italy
ANDREA APPIANI (1754–1817)
Oil on canvas, 1805

Emperor Francis I in coronation robes
LEOPOLD KUPELWIESER (1796–1862)
Oil on canvas

Honorary Medal of 1789
Silver
On 19 July, 1789, this decoration for bravery in gold and silver, for non-commissioned officers and other ranks, was established by Emperor Joseph II, following a proposal by Field Marshal Laudon. In 1809, it was renamed "Medal of Bravery". It was a token gratitude meant to encourage the common soldier; it was combined with an additional allowance.

Archduke Charles won the Battle of Aspern (21/22 May, 1809), but lost the Battle of Deutsch-Wagram (5/6 July, 1809), which decided the war. In the Peace of Schönbrunn, Austria again had to accept heavy territorial losses. Nevertheless, the Habsburg Monarchy joined a coalition of Russians, Prussians, Swedes, and the British.

Napoleon's fate was decided in the Battle of Leipzig between 16 October and 19 October, 1813. At the end of March 1814, the allies arrived in Paris, and Napoleon abdicated.

The Congress of Vienna, which took place between November 1814 and June 1815, served the purpose of reorganizing Europe. Napoleon's attempt at restoration, which ended with his defeat in the Battle of Waterloo and the exile of the French Emperor, was all but an *entr'acte*. On 20 November, 1815, the Second Peace Treaty of Paris was signed. Only a few years after the Congress of Vienna, however, many European countries were troubled by revolutionary movements caused by major social and national problems. For decades, Austria was to play the role of a kind of "European policeman",

thereby suppressing liberal movements inside its own borders, too.

What is known as the Austrian *"Biedermeier"*, was, on closer examination, a very violent time. Napoleon's son, the Duke of Reichstadt, who was growing up at the Imperial Court in the custody of his grandfather, was part of this period.

After the death of Emperor Francis I in 1835 his simple-minded son followed him; under the reign of Emperor Ferdinand I the situation worsened.

On 13 March, 1848, revolution finally broke out in the Austrian Empire as well. In Prague, the revolutionary movement was violently crushed. In Vienna, the rebels succeeded in forcing the Imperial and Royal troops stationed in the city to leave. It was not until October that the Imperial city was recaptured by Prince Alfred Windischgrätz and *Feldmarschall-Leutnant* Count Joseph Jellačić, using enormous military means. In Hungary and Italy, though, the situation remained extremely tense.

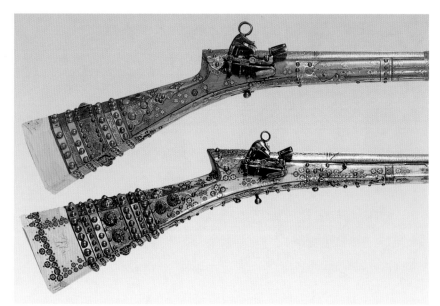

Turkish muskets

18th century

These muskets with a Miquelet lock, captured in the taking of Belgrade in 1789, are very richly ornamented. They probably originate from the possessions of high Ottoman dignitaries. Presumably Emperor-to-be Francis II/I brought these spoils of war to Vienna.

Uniformed figures of the Imperial Army of 1765 to 1799

HELMUT KRAUHS (1912–1995)

Height ca. 320 mm, 1955

These figures portray a private of the Hussar Regiment, a major-general, and a grenadier of the "Hungarian" Infantry Regiment. During the reign of Emperor Joseph II, uniforms showed striking innovations which were meticulously followed in the uniforms of the figures.

Stylized cap of liberty on blue, white, and red pole with a pike

Tin, end of the 18th century

This cap functioned as a "fortress flag"; it was captured by Austrian troops on 17 November, 1793 on the occasion of the taking of the Alsacian Fort of St Louis. The so-called Phrygian cap, which in classical antiquity indicated a freed slave, was the symbol of the most radical group of the French Revolution, the Jacobins.

French observation balloon

This balloon was probably the French balloon "Intrepide", one of six observation balloons used by the French army in special airship companies between 1794 and 1799. It was captured by Austrian troops after the Battle of Würzburg on 3 September, 1796.

Hooded military coat of an Imperial general in "German" uniform (left)

White cloth with scarlet lapels and cuffs, c. 1790

"Generals in German uniform" were a speciality of the Habsburg armies; it could be explained by the fact that they had to be distinguished from "generals in Hungarian uniform".

Uniform jacket worn by an Imperial war commissar (right)

White cloth with scarlet lapels and cuffs, c. 1792

The war commissars were civil servants. The nature of their tasks was exclusively economic. They were responsible for fiscal matters and the control of the administration of arms and other materials employed by the army.

Figure of a hussar of the Imperial Hussar Regiment Field Marshal Count Dagobert Siegmund Wurmser

Before 1798

During the First Coalition War against France (1792–1797) the light Austrian cavalry of the Hussars, who originally came from Hungary, still wore the uniforms that had been in use since the time of the army reforms of 1765. In the war of 1792 to 1797 against France, the regiment fought in the Netherlands, at the Rhine, and in northern Italy.

Battalion colour of the Imperial infantry, model of 1805
Yellow silk, armorial eagle painted in oil

The field of the flag shows the double eagle of the Holy Roman Empire with the Ottonic Crown, and the Austrian double eagle topped by two crowns in the centre. It clarifies that Emperor Francis, responding to Napoleon's aspirations to the imperial crown, assumed the title of Emperor of Austria in 1804. When Francis II resigned as a Holy Roman Emperor in 1806, once again a new flag for the Austrian Empire had to be created.

The silver cup of Olmütz
HANS KELLNER (1582[?]–1617)
Gold-plated silver. Height: 645 mm, after 1600

During the First Coalition War (1792–1797) against France, this richly decorated covered silver cup was handed over to Emperor Francis II by the Moravian town of Olmütz (Olomouc) as a voluntary contribution to the war effort. Unlike other precious works of art, however, it was not melted down, but preserved in memory of the people's readiness to make sacrifices.

Standard of the Second Squadron of the 15ᵗʰ French Imperial Dragoon Regiment

Silk, painted, c. 1804

Napoleon was the creator of this new type of standard. On 5 December, 1804, the first "Aigles" were publicly issued to the various units.

Andreas Hofer

Attributed to JOHANN GEORG SCHEDLER (1777–1866)

Water colour on silk

Andreas Hofer (1767–1810), leader of the Tyrolese, was one of the most popular figures of the Austrian struggle against Napoleon. In 1808, a plan for insurrection of the Tyrol against Bavarian rule was devised. In 1809, the rebellion broke out. The Tyrolese, under the command of Andreas Hofer, were victorious in three battles at Berg Isel. The fourth battle was lost. Hofer was taken prisoner. In 1810, he was summarily shot at Mantua.

Staff of the colours of the First Battalion of the 15th Imperial Infantry Regiment Baron Zach from the Battle of Aspern on 21/22 May, 1809 (with laurel wreath and plaque)

On the morning of 22 May, 1809, the Austrian centre began to totter. Napoleon ordered a breakthrough by employing the French cavalry. The Austrian grenadiers yielded ground. Apparently, Archduke Charles, together with the standard-bearer of the First Battalion of the 15th Infantry Regiment, managed to close the lines again, and to advance the centre. The battle was won.

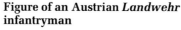

Figure of an Austrian *Landwehr* infantryman

1809

The uniform consisted of a so-called "corsé hat" with white-edging, a dun mid-calf length coat, white linen trousers, and black cloth gaiters. The insignia of rank of a soldier of these territorial reserve units consisted of a corporal's baton. The *Landwehr* was created by an Imperial directive of 9 June, 1808, as a complement to the Imperial and Royal army.

Archduke Charles in the Battle of Aspern

JOHANN PETER KRAFFT (1780–1856)

Oil on canvas, 1812

This famous episode from the Battle of Aspern, when Archduke Charles reached for the flag of the Infantry Regiment Zach No 15, inspired Krafft to paint the picture.

He consciously chose the pose that Jacques-Louis David had set as a pattern with his picture "Bonaparte on St Bernard" in 1801.

The picture of the Archduke holding the standard thus became a conventional image.

Napoleon's pouch

Tanned leather

This bag with several compartments could be attached to the saddle by its leather straps. On its outside, there are two brass plates displaying the following inscriptions: "Dépêches de sa Majesté Napoléon Empereur et Roi" and "Départ de Paris pour le Quartier Général" (departure from Paris to the main quarters).

Reporting victory after the Battle of Leipzig on 18 October, 1813

JOHANN PETER KRAFFT (1780–1856)

Oil on canvas, 1817 (from the Military Home for Invalids in Vienna)

The commander-in-chief of the allied armies, Field Marshal Prince Karl Schwarzenberg (1771–1820), reports victory over Napoleon in the Battle of Leipzig to the allied monarchs Tsar Alexander I of Russia, Emperor Francis I of Austria, and King Frederick William III of Prussia (from left to right)

Star for the Grand Cross of the Military Order of Maria Theresa

Enamelled silver, 1st half of the 19th century

Ornamental cases for the Metal Army Cross of Emperor Francis I

Gilded bronze covered with red satin; with insignia and coat of arms on the lid and engraved inscriptions on the inside of the lid

The Metal Army Cross of 1813/14, also called "Cannon Cross", was established in 1814 by Emperor Francis I for all participants in the Wars of Liberation; it was cast from captured French cannons and was the first general decoration.

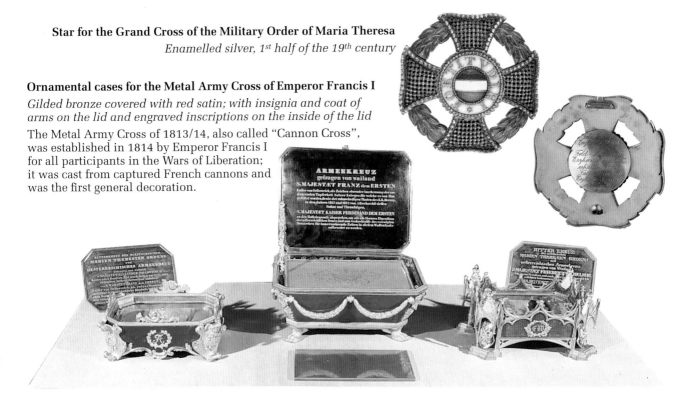

The return of the *Landwehr* Infantryman

JOHANN PETER KRAFFT (1780–1856)

Oil on canvas, 1820

As early as 1813, in response to the Wars of Liberation, Krafft created the "Parting of the *Landwehr* Infantryman". Commissioned by the Emperor, "The return of the *Landwehr* Infantryman" was designed as a companion piece. The soldier, having arrived home unscathed, has been awarded the "Medal of Bravery" and is proudly welcomed by his family. These two pictures already introduce the genre-painting of the Biedermeier period. They were used to stress the importance of arming the populace against Napoleon.

Coat of Russian General Count Shuvalov

Dun cloth

This officer's coat was worn by Napoleon during his passage into exile on the isle of Elba from 25 to 27 April, 1814. The disguise was a precautionary measure; it was feared that he might be assassinated.

Archduke Charles with his children on the terrace of the Weilburg at Baden near Vienna

JOHANN NEPOMUK ENDER (1793–1854)

Oil on canvas, 1832

Archduke Charles amongst his children on the terrace of Weilburg castle near Baden. The castle, which no longer exists, had been named after Charles's wife, Henriette von Nassau-Weilburg, who died in 1829. Her bust can be seen on the left.

The Duke of Reichstadt

Adapted from MORITZ MICHAEL DAFFINGER
(1790–1849)

Water colour

Napoleon II Francis Joseph Charles
(1811–1832), the only son of Napoleon
I from his second marriage with Austrian
Archduchess Marie Louise, is portrayed in
the white uniform jacket of a staff officer of
the 60th Imperial and Royal Infantry
Regiment "Prinz Gustav von Wasa". He
managed to rise to the rank of colonel but
died of pulmonary tuberculosis at a very
young age.

Paintbox of the Duke of Reichstadt

This paintbox contains compartments with
English water colours. The miniature in the
centre, showing a view of the city of Vienna,
is by BALTHASAR WIGAND (1771–1846), in
his time the most renowned painter of city
views and landscapes.

Portrait of Austrian State Chancellor Metternich
ANONYMOUS
Oil on canvas, at the beginning of 19th century

At the Congress of Vienna in 1815, Prince Clemens Lothar Metternich (1773–1859) played a leading role in the reorganization of Europe. He was appointed State Chancellor in 1821. His fierce opposition to national and liberal movements induced him to counteract the trends of the time. If it seemed necessary to him, he even employed the army. The revolution of March 1848 led to his dismissal.

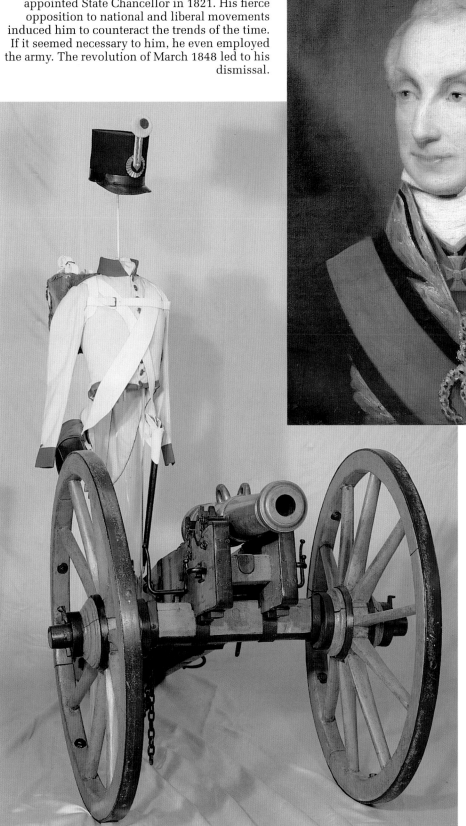

Uniform of the Austrian 4th Infantry Regiment *Hoch- und Deutschmeister* for a child, and a miniaturized field gun (one-pounder)

This uniform was worn by Archduke Francis Joseph, the future Emperor, during his military instruction in 1843. The miniaturized field cannon was used for practical military training of the Austrian archdukes.

Dolmans for a general of the Hungarian army, and for a senior officer of the 4th Hussar Regiment, complete with scabbards for sabres

The left dolman belonged to the commander of the Imperial and Royal army in Hungary, *Feldmarschall-Leutnant* Count Franz Philipp Lamberg, who was assassinated by Hungarian revolutionaries on the bridge between Pest and Ofen (today Budapest) on 28 September, 1848. The right dolman (model of 1840) is fitted with a bandoleer.

Memorabilia from the revolution of 1848/49 (National Guard, Academic Legion, Honvéd Army)

Colour of an Imperial infantry regiment, model of 1816

White silk

The field flag bears the Austrian double eagle with Imperial crown and red crown bands; also a "Madonna immaculate" in white garment together with blue cape.
Military flags and standards were always sacred symbols of the state. The standard bearers had to defend them at risk of their lives. In the Habsburg army, this standard signified the highest-ranking formation within an infantry regiment.

National Guard parading on Platz am Hof in Vienna in 1848

ANONYMOUS

Oil on copper

Owing to the revolutionary events of March 1848, it became possible to establish a National Guard. Apart from members of this formation, the picture shows the building of the former civil armoury (in the centre), and the Ministry of War. In October 1848, Minister of War Latour was assassinated on this square.

Hall 4 | Field Marshal Radetzky and His Time
(1848–1866)

In 1848, the outbreak of revolution once again seemed to form the prelude to the disintegration of the Austrian Empire. The Kingdom of Sardinia-Piedmont took the revolutionary events in Lombardy and in Venetia as an opportunity to declare war on Austria. In Hungary, revolutionary and national forces formed and began to march towards Vienna. Only after deploying all available military forces was it possible to put down the revolution and conduct war on two fronts. The engagement thereby sometimes took on the characteristics of a blitzkrieg. Field Marshal Radetzky, the supreme commander in the area, defeated the Sardinian-Piedmontese army in a number of skirmishes and battles, and called a truce which was renounced by Sardinia in 1849. Once again Radetzky achieved victories at Mortara and Novara, which brought about peace at least for a few years. Yet Hungary was different. Fighting there dragged on all winter and most of the year 1849 and could only be stopped through the cooperation of Austrian troops

with a Russian contingent. On 2 December, 1848, Emperor Ferdinand I abdicated the throne in favour of his nephew, Francis Joseph. Thus began the Francisco-Josephinian era, which lasted for 68 years and was marked by a war at the beginning and one at the end.

After the victories in Italy and Hungary, the young Emperor strove to consolidate the empire again, and to establish a strong, centralized government. He was only partly successful. In the Lombardo-Venetian Kingdom, Field Marshal Radetzky embodied this central rule up to as late as 1858. At the age of ninety, however, he was replaced and relegated to myth before long. Francis Joseph tried to continue using the Austrian army as an instrument to maintain or restore order in Europe. He did so in 1850 against Prussia, in 1853 against Montenegro, and in the Crimean War of 1854 to 1856. In 1859, Austria suffered its first resounding defeat in another war against Sardinia-Piedmont, which was allied with France. After the Battles of Ma-

Emperor Francis Joseph I in the uniform of a Colonel and proprietor of the 3rd Dragoon Regiment

IGNAZ KREPP (1801–1853)

Oil on canvas

Field Marshal Count Joseph Radetzky

GEORG DECKER (1819–1894)

Oil on canvas

Emperor Francis Joseph I

ALBRECHT (1786–1862) and FRANZ ADAM (1815–1866)

Oil on canvas, 1856

The painting shows one of the earliest portrayals of Emperor Francis Joseph (1830–1916) in his capacity as commander-in-chief of the Imperial army. The magnificent frame is crowned by a pair of griffins and the Imperial coat of arms. The corners show the arms of Hungary, Bohemia, Austria below the Enns, and Lombardo-Venetia.

genta and Solferino, the Habsburg Monarchy lost Lombardy. The consequences of the defeat were that Austria was gradually transformed into a constitutional monarchy. While neo-absolutism became a thing of the past, endeavours to use the army as a force to maintain order in Europe were not.

In 1864, Austria and Prussia combined to go to war against Denmark. The conflict was about the two German-speaking principalities of Schleswig and Holstein, both of which were under Danish administration. The Austrians under *Feldmarschall-Leutnant* Baron Ludwig von Gablenz achieved military successes near Oeversee and Veile. Holstein was put under Austrian, and Schleswig under Prussian control. The victors quarreled over the two territories. The reasons for the conflict lay much deeper, though. On 8 April, 1866, Prussia formed a league against Austria with the Kingdom of Italy. Under the command of Archduke Albrecht, the southern army of the Austrians was

victorious near Custoza (south of Lake Garda) on 24 June, 1866. But the war was decided in the north. After a number of ill-fated skirmishes, the Austrian Army under *Feldzeugmeister* Ludwig von Benedek suffered a devastating defeat near Königgrätz (Hradec Králové, east of Prague; the battle is also called Battle of Sadová) on 3 July. The Peace Treaty of Prague pushed the Austrian Empire out of the German Confederation for good. It kept only its positions in the eastern part of central Europe and in south-eastern Europe.

Apart from the destinies of the respective countries, the fates of individuals also stand out again and again. Among these individuals was Archduke Ferdinand Maximilian, brother of the young Emperor, who, through French intercession, adopted the crown of the Mexican Empire in 1864. Yet he failed to build up a new Habsburg dynasty in Mexico or to rule the country in peace. He was defeated in a battle against Mexican troops under Benito Juárez, captured, and shot in 1867.

Pistols used by the Lombardo-Venetian guards

This type of officers' pistols with holsters was used by members of the Lombardo-Venetian aristocratic guards. Established in 1839, the reliability of these Italian-speaking guards was doubted during the revolutionary battles of 1848/49. In 1849 they were therefore considerably reduced in numbers, and in 1856 it was decided to disband them altogether.

Cup of honour for the poet and dramatist Franz Grillparzer

Goldsmith's Studio Josef Türck & Sohn

Gilded Silver, 1849

This goblet, decorated with symbols of poetry and war, was presented to Grillparzer in 1850 by *Feldzeugmeister* Baron von Hess and Prime Minister Prince Schwarzenberg. The reason for this honouring was Grillparzer's "Ode to Radetzky". Its introductory words, "Hail to thee, my leader, go forth and strike! Not just for the sake of glory, in thy camp is Austria …", became the hallmark of the Imperial and Royal army.

Trumpet presented to the 10th *Feldjäger* Battalion "Kopal"

Produced according to the instructions on uniforms of 1840. Behind the mouthpiece there is a silver double eagle wearing a small gold crown, holding a cartouche with the following inscriptions in his left talon: *"Monte Berico"* and *"Kopal ruft"*. This trumpet was presented to the 10th *Feldjäger* Battalion for the storming of Monte Berico (near Vicenza, 10 June, 1848), during which the commander of the battalion, Colonel Kopal, fell.

The Battle of Novara on 23 March, 1849

ALBRECHT ADAM (1786–1862)

Oil on canvas, 1855

This picture shows the victory of Field Marshal Radetzky leading the Imperial army over the Piedmontese under King Albert of Sardinia. The victories at Mortara and Novara (west of Milan) decided the war against Italy. The painting was a present by the officers of the *Generalquartiermeisterstab* to Radetzky's chief of general staff, *Feldzeugmeister* Baron von Hess, to mark his completion of fifty years' service.

Austrian rocket launcher for eight-pounder spin-stabilized rockets

1865

Refining the construction of the British designer Halle, rocket stabilization was no longer achieved by attaching a shaft, but by the propellant itself. After ignition, gas was discharged not only through the nozzle, but also through lateral drill-holes to achieve a spin.

Old-age portrait of Field Marshal Radetzky

Photograph by Maurizio LOTZE, Verona

Field Marshal Count Johann Josef Wenzel Radetzky von Radetz (1766–1858), who, as chief of the *Generalquartiermeisterstab*, contributed notably to the decisive victory over Napoleon in the Battle of Leipzig as early as 1813, and who was Commander General in the Kingdom of Lombardo-Venetia since 1831, attained his greatest successes in the years of the revolution of 1848/49. He remained active army commander and civil and military governor-general up to the age of 91.

Field Marshal Radetzky's letter of resignation, sabre, and Order of the Golden Fleece

After his victories at Santa Lucia, Custoza (1848), Mortara, Novara, and Venice (1849) Field Marshal Radetzky was awarded the highest honours and decorations. Among them was the sabre (designed by the architect Eduard van der Nüll) presented to him by the Vienna National Guard. In December 1856, the elderly governor-general of the kingdom of Lombardo-Venetia tendered his resignation to the emperor. It was accepted two months later. The letter of resignation is in his own handwriting.

Evacuation of wounded men after the Battle of Solferino on 24 June, 1859

HANS VON MARÉES (1837–1887) – *Oil on canvas, 1860*

On 24 June, 1859, the allied French and Piedmontese troops won a victory at Solferino over the Austrian army led by the young Emperor Francis Joseph. The enormous toll of lives on both sides initiated the Geneva Convention of 1864, and the establishment of the Red Cross by the Swiss Henri Dunant.

The battery of the dead

VACLAV SOCHOR (1855–1935) – *Oil on canvas, 1901/7*

This monumental painting illustrates the end of the cavalry battery of the Austrian 8th Field Artillery Regiment in the Battle of Königgrätz (Hradec Králové) on 3 July, 1866. The Austrian northern army under the command of *Feldzeugmeister* Ludwig von Benedek had advanced as far as Königgrätz in the war against Prussia. The main battle was decided near Chlum. On this day, Benedek lost 44,000 men, 5,650 of whom were killed.

Lorenz and Dreyse (needle-)gun

With the needle-gun (below) the Prussian army already possessed an efficient breech-loader in the Battle of Königgrätz (Hradec Králové) on 3 July, 1866. This weapon was clearly superior in rate of fire (cadence) to the Austrian muzzle-loaders of the *Lorenz* system (above).

The artillery reserve unit after the Battle of Königgrätz (Hradec Králové) on 3 July, 1866

RUDOLF RITTER OTTO VON OTTEN-FELD (1856–1913)

Oil on canvas, 1897

While suffering heavy losses, the artillery reserve covered the orderly retreat of the Austrian northern army across the river Elbe.

Four-pounder field cannon, model of 1863

This cannon was the standard gun employed by the Austrian army in the wars of 1864 and 1866. It proved superior to the opponents' gun types with regard to accuracy and mobility.

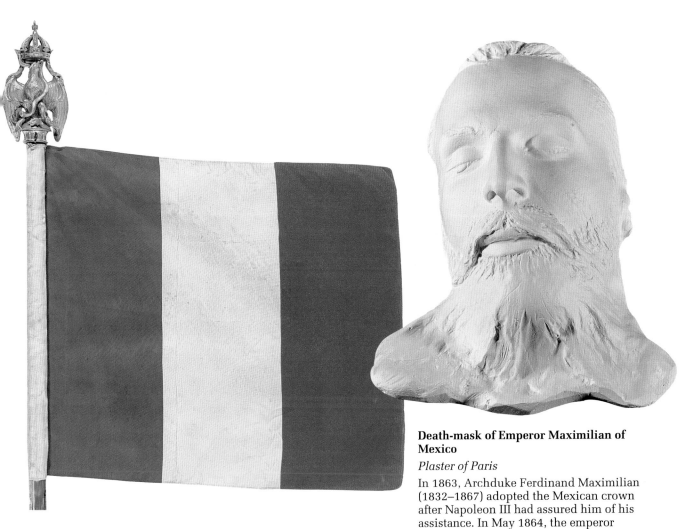

Death-mask of Emperor Maximilian of Mexico

Plaster of Paris

In 1863, Archduke Ferdinand Maximilian (1832–1867) adopted the Mexican crown after Napoleon III had assured him of his assistance. In May 1864, the emperor arrived in Mexico. However, he soon realized that the military and economic problems there could not be resolved. When Napoleon ended his assistance in 1866, Maximilian's cause was lost. He was encircled by the troops of Benito Juárez in Querétaro, captured, tried, sentenced by court martial, and shot on 19 June, 1867.

Standard of the Imperial Mexican Hussar Regiment (1865–1867), and cartridge (below) for a cavalry officer of the Austro-Mexican volunteer brigade (1864–1867)

Both the Hussar regiment and the volunteer brigade recruited from former members of the Austrian army, who had followed Emperor Maximilian to Mexico in 1864.

Hall 5 | Francis Joseph Hall and Sarajevo

From the Establishment of the Austro-Hungarian Dual Monarchy in 1867 to the Outbreak of the First World War in 1914

Austria's defeat in 1866 had far-reaching consequences for the Habsburg Monarchy. It lost its political influence on the German states and Italy, and implemented a structural reform which led to the establishment of a dualist system *("Ausgleich")*. Under this reform, the relationship of the countries under the Hungarian crown to the rest of the Empire was redefined. The Habsburg Monarchy was divided into two parts, the Austrian countries ("Cisleithania"; west of the Leitha river) and the countries of the Hungarian crown ("Transleithania"; east of the Leitha river). From 1867 onward, there were only three areas that were considered common concerns of the Empire: foreign affairs, finance, and the military. The settlement had most far-reaching consequences for the military, since it became divided along with the Empire. As a result, there was the common Imperial and Royal *("kaiserlich und königlich"; "k. u. k.")* army and the Imperial and Royal navy. In addition, the Royal-Hungarian *("königlich-ungarisch"; "k. u.") Honvéd* was established in the Hungarian half of the Empire and the Imperial-Royal *("kaiserlich-königlich"; "k. k.") Landwehr* in the Austrian half. The look of the army thus subdivided into three parts manifested itself in many ways.

This look was not only limited to the so-called "magic of the uniform" typical of the Austro-Hungarian troops. The armed forces of the Habsburg Monarchy were much more successful when it came to integrating the various peoples of the Empire. In the regiments of the common army, the *Landwehr*, and the *Honvéd*, not only were members of all nationalities proportionally represented, but so were members of all religious denominations and social classes. The "Imperial and Royal" army stood for the unity of the Empire, as did the civil service, and, ultimately, the Emperor and King. The period of peace that lasted from 1867 to 1914 was only interrupted by one major military event,

Emperor Francis Joseph I

Friedrich FRANCESCHINI
(1845–1906)

Oil on canvas

Archduke Francis Ferdinand

Wilhelm VITA (1846–1919)

Oil on canvas

Archduke Ferdinand is here shown wearing the Order of Maria Theresa, the Order of Leopold and the Order of the Iron Crown, along with the Order of St. Stephen. Wearing these decorations was actually not a privilege of the heir to the throne. Like the honorary rank of field marshal, wearing these decorations anticipates the time after his accession to the throne.

Faded fanfares

Ludwig KOCH (1866–1934)

Oil on canvas, 1932

After having spent many years in the garrison town of Enns, the trumpet corps, heading the 6th dragoon regiment, turns into the Wiener Straße in May 1908. In the background of the main square, one can discern regimental commander Colonel Baron Vinzenz von Abele.

the occupational campaign *("Okkupationsfeldzug")* of 1878. Back then, the Austro-Hungarian troops, under the leadership of *Feldzeugmeister* Phillipović, occupied the Ottoman provinces of Bosnia and Herzegovina. This occupation became an annexation in 1908. Generally speaking, Austria-Hungary was only indirectly involved in the struggles over political power in Europe. It relied on the alliance that had first been established with the German Empire in 1879 and was later extended to Italy in 1882. Since 1908, however, Austria increasingly has become dragged into the conflicts centred in the Balkans. After a few decades, it became clear that the settlement of 1867 had not brought a satisfying solution for the Habsburg Empire and that the demands of the major nationalities – which numbered eleven altogether – could only be met by another radical reform of the Empire's structure. The hope for a positive outcome of such an endeavour was first centred

around Crown Prince Rudolph and, after his death, around the new heir to the throne, Archduke Francis Ferdinand. Although the latter had not yet been assigned any political tasks by Emperor Francis Joseph, he had received military assignments and was to be commander-in-chief in the event of war. Francis Ferdinand was, however, interested in keeping Austria-Hungary out of war, not least because he wanted to implement the reform of the Empire. However, the voices of those who asserted that the Habsburg Monarchy no longer met contemporary needs and that it could only be reformed partially increased. Nonetheless, new settlements were continually negotiated in order to balance the interests and peculiarities of the peoples within the Habsburg monarchy as a whole. Finally, however, all of these attempts were rendered futile in one moment: when Francis Ferdinand came to Sarajevo, he and his wife Sophie von Hohenberg were assassinated by a Serb nationalist on 28 June, 1914.

Uniform coat of a Major of the Austrian 33rd Landwehr Infantry Battalion (1869–1889)

Dark blue cloth with scarlet lapel and sleeve cuffs and silver buttons with the battalion number "33"

The Bohemian *Landwehr* Infantry Battalion No 33 was stationed in Prague and, like the 28th Imperial and Royal Bohemian Infantry Regiment, was supplied from Prague.

Officer's uniform coat and fez of the Austro-Hungarian infantry from Bosnia-Herzegovina

Uniform coat of light blue fabric with so-called "alizarin"-red lapel and sleeve cuffs and gold-plated buttons with the regiment number "2", fez of madder red fabric with black tassel

Since 1882, the Austro-Hungarian army has included troops from Bosnia-Herzegovina. Until the First World War, four Bosnian regiments had been established that soon earned a reputation for exceptional courage and served as elite units within the Austro-Hungarian army during the war.

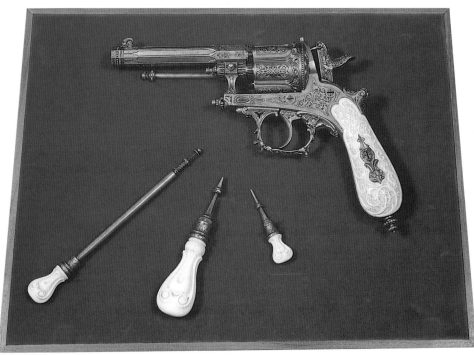

Representational revolver with accessories of Crown Prince Rudolph

This revolver, with a 9-mm calibre, was dedicated to the Crown Prince by the Gasser company. Crown Prince Rudolph (1858–1889) had always been expected to pursue a military career. He finally attained the rank of *Feldmarschall-Leutnant*. His interests, however, were not in the military. As chairman of the former army museum committee, Crown Prince Rudolph distinguished himself by rebuilding the museum.

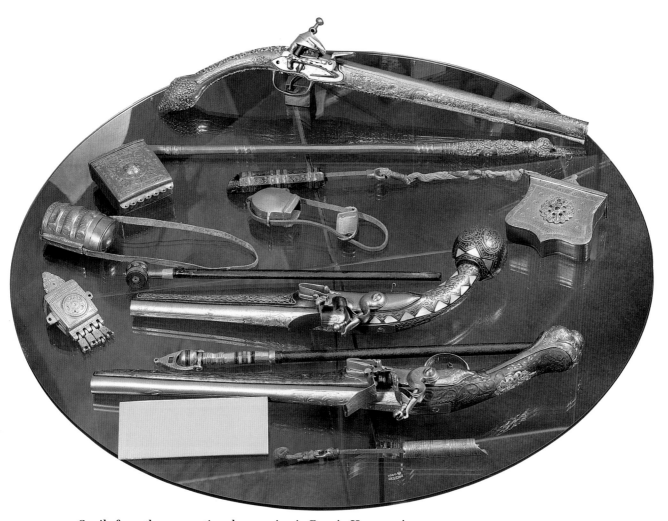

Spoils from the occupational campaign in Bosnia-Herzegovina

These pistols of Turkish make are traditional firearms whose elaborate adornments indicate that they were less intended for military use than for decorative purposes. The decorations suggest that the pistols were made in the 17th and 18th centuries.

Austro-Hungarian field marshal's uniform of Emperor Francis Joseph I

This so-called "campagne" uniform jacket with scarlet cuffs and golden braid trimmings with acanthus leaf ornaments was worn with the everyday uniform, while the dress uniform jacket of white fabric with scarlet cuffs and field marshal braid trimmings was worn only on special occasions. Emperor Francis Joseph I wore these uniforms in his role as commander-in-chief of the Austro-Hungarian army.

Military priests

OSKAR BRÜCH (1869–1943)

Oil on canvas, from photograph, 1895

The picture belongs to a series of 34, painted for the 1896 millennial exhibition in Budapest, showing Austro-Hungarian army uniforms. In the painting, a Catholic military priest in a formal uniform, a winter marching uniform, and a dress uniform, a Protestant military priest in dress uniform, and an Apostolic field vicar in dress uniform can be seen. In addition, Orthodox priests, imams, and rabbis were part of the Austro-Hungarian army.

Figure of a sergeant of the Royal Hungarian Guards in ceremonial uniform

Ca. 1910

Since its establishment by Maria Theresa in 1760, the Hungarian guard served the Habsburgs in their role as Kings of Hungary and Grand Princes of Transylvania. The uniform shows many elements from the Hungarian national costume: a *kalpak* of brown fur with a pouch of green fabric and a crest of white heron feathers, an *attila* with silver cord embellishments and ornamental embroidery, elaborately embroidered trousers and yellow Hungarian leather riding boots. The leopard skin, worn across the left shoulder, is also typical of this uniform.

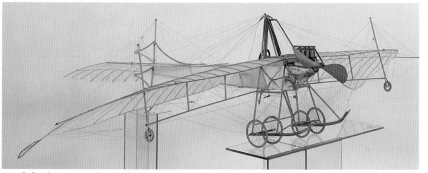

Model of an *Etrich Taube* (type A II)

Technical innovations in the Austro-Hungarian army

Before 1914

Since the turn of the 20th century, the Austro-Hungarian army experienced a considerable trend towards modernization. The introduction of more efficient machine guns, the birth of military aviation, and an improved food supply through field kitchens helped to secure army standards. Several technical innovations, however, failed because of financial difficulties and were never implemented or only put into practice during the First World War.

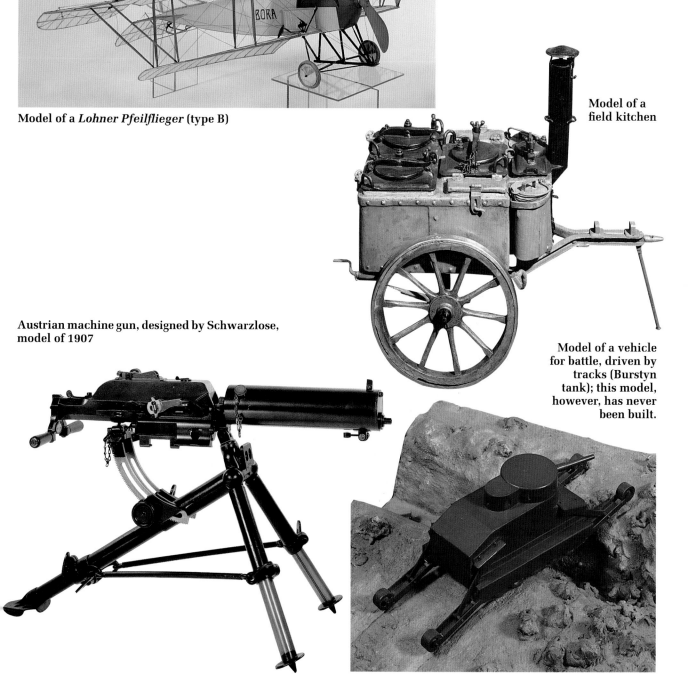

Model of a *Lohner Pfeilflieger* (type B)

Model of a field kitchen

Austrian machine gun, designed by Schwarzlose, model of 1907

Model of a vehicle for battle, driven by tracks (Burstyn tank); this model, however, has never been built.

Helmet of a member of the First Imperial-Royal *Arcière* Guards, model of 1898

Silver helmet (here without the typical crest of white buffalo hair) with brim and neck screen, double-headed eagle with half-opened wings as well as the Imperial coat of arms in gold-plated bronze

The *Arcière* Guards were the most distinguished among the guards; they were not troops in the usual sense, but military units belonging to the Imperial household, whose security tasks and ceremonial duties concerned the monarch and his family.

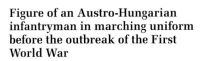

Figure of an Austro-Hungarian infantryman in marching uniform before the outbreak of the First World War

The efficiency of weapons having been improved enormously in the meantime, the pike-grey uniform was introduced in 1908 to large parts of the army in order to camouflage soldiers in action. The infantryman is equipped with a knapsack with a fur cover, a cartridge-box, a spade with sheath, and two pairs of ammunition pouches. For a weapon, he carries a repeating rifle of the *Mannlicher* system, model of 1895, with a bayonet.

Alpine equipment of the Austrian *Landwehr* mountain troops and mementoes of Theodor von Lerch

Ca. 1910

Austria-Hungary was one of the first countries in the world to establish mountain troops. Their equipment included skis, nailed mountain boots, crampons, ice axes, alpenstocks, climbing ropes, snowshoes, etc. In 1911, First Lieutenant Theodor von Lerch was invited to Japan to teach Alpine skiing to Japanese soldiers. This also started the development of skiing as a popular recreational sport in Japan.

Archduke Francis Ferdinand's uniform and chaiselongue, on which the successor to the Austrian throne died on 28 June, 1914

Archduke Francis Ferdinand (1863–1914) and his wife, Duchess Sophie von Hohenberg, were mortally wounded by pistol shots fired by assassin Gavrilo Princip during their ride through Sarajevo. The projectile, fired from a Browning pistol, tore Francis Ferdinand's jugular vein and injured his windpipe. On the jacket and the trousers, significant traces of blood are still visible. Francis Ferdinand died without ever regaining consciousness.

The Sarajevo car

Passenger vehicle, make Graef & Stift, built in 1910, 4 cylinders, 28/32 hp. Left of the windshield, there is a small banner with the insignia of the Archduke

After the assassination at Sarajevo, the car was inpounded. The owner, Count Francis Harrach, donated it to Emperor Francis Joseph, who ordered the vehicle to be moved to the Imperial and Royal Army Museum. From 1914 to 1944, the vehicle was on display in the Hall of the Generals. Around the end of the Second World War, it was damaged, and, after undergoing repairs, was placed in its current location where it has been since 1957.

Hall 6 | The First World War and the End of the Habsburg Monarchy 1914–1918

Austria-Hungary interpreted the assassination of Archduke Francis Ferdinand and his wife in Sarajevo as solely the fault of Serbia; a fault that could only be redeemed by the subjugation of this Balkan state. The Danube Monarchy set an ultimatum. Serbia mobilized its troops and was supported by Russia. Thus, a regional war became a war between different allies: by the end of July 1914, Austria-Hungary, the German Empire, and, in October 1914, the Ottoman Empire on one side (i.e., the Central Powers), Serbia, Russia, and Russia's allies France and Great Britain (i.e., the Entente) on the other. For Austria-Hungary, the military actions mainly focused on the Balkans and on Galicia. The German Empire, however, tried to subjugate France. Austria-Hungary failed in Serbia and Galicia, just as the German Empire failed in the west. By the end of 1914, Germans and Austrians already had depleted all their resources so as not to be overpowered by Russians troops. Not until the cru-

cial Battle of Tarnów-Gorlice was the most imminent danger under control. The losses of the Austro-Hungarian army, however, were disproportionally high. And still, there was no end to the war in sight. On the contrary: in May 1915, Italy, a country that, up to that point, had been an ally of the Habsburg Monarchy, also declared war on Austria-Hungary. Thus, a military front line was established in the southwest, reaching from the South Tyrol and the high mountain region to the area of Görz (Gorizia) and Trieste.

The First World War, however, was not a conflict limited to front lines. It was a war between different industries that focused on the nutrition of the people; thus, everybody literally experienced the consequences of the war with their own bodies. For a long time, it even seemed that the military aspect of the war would least harm Austria-Hungary. By the end of 1915, Serbia was defeated by a fourth offensive strike that also included German and

General of the infantry Baron Franz Conrad von Hötzendorf
HERMANN TORGGLER (1878–1939)
Oil on canvas

Emperor Charles I as Field Marshal in field uniform
WILHELM VICTOR KRAUSZ (1878–1959)
Oil on canvas, 1917

Austrian 70-mm mountain gun, model of 1899, the so-called "Ortler gun"

With Italy's entry into the war in May 1915, fighting also moved to the high mountain region. The artillery had to move into positions of up to 3,800 m in height.

Bulgarian troops. Austro-Hungarian troops forced Montenegro to capitulate and then invaded Albania. At the beginning of 1916, Austria-Hungary failed to launch an offensive from the South Tyrol and defeat Italy. Until the end of 1917, one battle after the other had to be fought at the Isonzo river. In the east, however, Austria-Hungary and its allies managed to hold off the danger posed by the Russian army until the revolutions of 1917 forced Russia into an armistice and finally into the peace treaty of Brest-Litovsk. Austria-Hungary also managed to defeat Romania, which had declared war on the Central Powers in August 1916. In October and November 1917, during the 12th Isonzo battle, Germans and Austrians also had major military successes against Italy. Yet, the military situation distracted from increasingly deteriorating domestic conditions within the German Empire, and, even more so, within Austria-Hungary. In 1917, the food crisis assumed catastrophic dimensions. Austria-

Hungary, which had to struggle with substantial conflicts over nationality issues even during times of peace, became more and more threatened with disintegration. After Emperor Francis Joseph's death in November 1916, his successor, Emperor Charles I (1887–1922), tried to reach a peace agreement, but remained unsuccessful. In 1918, strikes and mutiny started to break out. Finally, Austria-Hungary attempted to force a military decision by means of a last offensive that started on 15 June, 1918. This "Piave" offensive, however, failed. In the autumn of 1918, the Habsburg Monarchy began to collapse and the breakdown of the army could not be prevented. On 3 November, 1918, Austria-Hungary signed an armistice at the Villa Giusti near Padua. At this point in time, various national successor states had already been formed. The political landscape of Europe had changed.

Prototype of a regimental colour for the Imperial and Royal regiments of infantry

Design 1915

The flag shows the so-called "middle common coat of arms" of Austria-Hungary with the Latin motto *"indivisibiliter ac inseparabiliter"* as well as the Austrian middle crest with the Emperor's crown, and the Hungarian crest with the King's crown. They are connected by the crest of Habsburg-Austria-Lorraine. The flag should have been manufactured after the war; yet, this plan was never put in practice.

Austrian 380-mm howitzer, model of 1916

This field howitzer, which belongs to the heaviest kind of artillery, was one of the most innovative weapons of the Austro-Hungarian army. Built in the Škoda works near Pilsen (Plzen) from 1916 to 1917, the projectiles, each weighing over 700 kg, could be fired at a distance of up to 15 km.

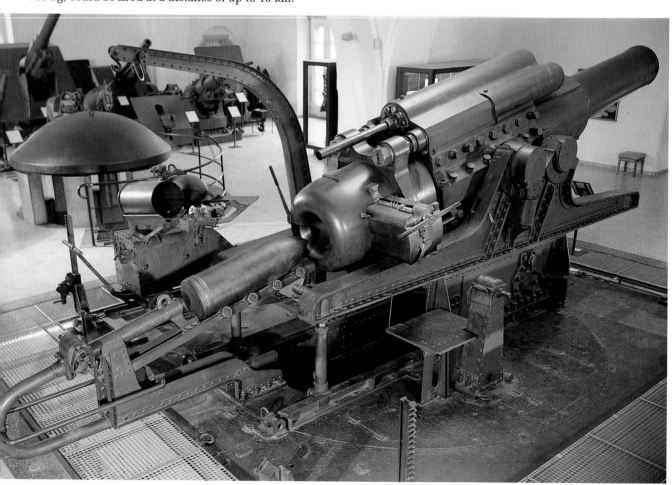

"To the unknown soldiers of 1914"

ALBIN EGGER-LIENZ (1868–1926)

Tempera on canvas, 1916

The assault on Uhnów during the fighting in Galicia inspired the painter to create several versions on the theme of the "storming soldiers". In the last version, the head bandages were substituted for steel helmets, which had been introduced in 1916. The East-Tyrolian artist created a symbol of modern mass warfare with this painting, which shows how each soldier could be replaced at random due to the loss of his identity.

Wooden signboard with a Russian revolutionary appeal for the Austro-Hungarian and German troops, 1917

Dating from the time of the Russian February and October revolution, this sign was put up at the frontline by Russian soldiers who were already fatigued by the war and heavily influenced by revolutionary Bolshevist ideas. The "bloody emperor", who should be overthrown like the Tsar, probably should have been the German Emperor William II.

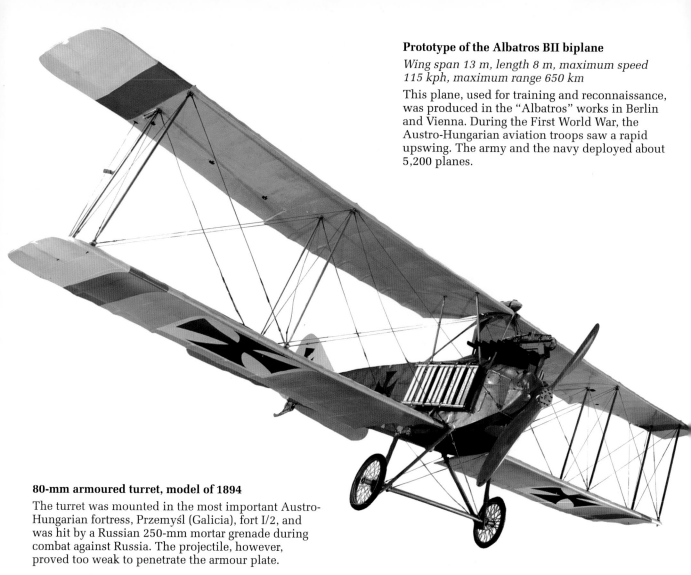

Prototype of the Albatros BII biplane

Wing span 13 m, length 8 m, maximum speed 115 kph, maximum range 650 km

This plane, used for training and reconnaissance, was produced in the "Albatros" works in Berlin and Vienna. During the First World War, the Austro-Hungarian aviation troops saw a rapid upswing. The army and the navy deployed about 5,200 planes.

80-mm armoured turret, model of 1894

The turret was mounted in the most important Austro-Hungarian fortress, Przemyśl (Galicia), fort I/2, and was hit by a Russian 250-mm mortar grenade during combat against Russia. The projectile, however, proved too weak to penetrate the armour plate.

Steel helmets from the First World War

Steel helmets were introduced due to the high number of head injuries by grenade and stone fragments. The first Austrian helmet prototypes, produced by the *Berndorfer Metallwarenfabrik* (right), were not satisfactory. Only the steel helmet, which imitates a German model (left) and was produced by German machines in Austrian factories in 1917/18, was acceptable.

Austro-Hungarian gas mask from the First World War

The use of poison gas since 1916 made it necessary to introduce light respirators. The mask was designed to protect against different kinds of poison gas. For this reason, the mask had a screw-on filter with various layers. The face protection consisted of rubberized linen.

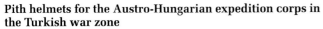

Pith helmets for the Austro-Hungarian expedition corps in the Turkish war zone

After the Ottoman Empire entered the war on 29 October, 1914, Austria-Hungary sent motor vehicle and artillery units to the Palestinian front for support. These units were supplied with tropical helmets as protection against the heat.

Captured Serbs before being transported

FERDINAND ANDRI (1871–1956)

Colour chalk on cardboard

After the fourth offensive against Serbia in October and November 1915, large parts of the Serbian army were taken prisoners of war. In this picture, Andri, who actually specialized in landscape and genre painting, shows the despair and hopelessness of a defeated unit.

Appeal "Our Army Needs Metal!" and *Deutschmeister* in Iron" (below)

The original expectation that the war would not last for long backfired during the First World War – especially for the Central Powers. For the armaments industry in particular, the shortage of raw material became more and more oppressive. The civilian population was therefore encouraged to sell (as with this poster) or donate metal (through patriotic war metal collection).

Field blouse made from shoddy

Due to the increasing shortage of raw material in Austria-Hungary, uniforms also had to be produced from substitute materials, among them the fibre from stinging nettles.

"Heimat – Dein Mann"

KARL STERRER (1885–1972)

*Blending technique
watercolour on paper, 1916*

Like Johann Peter Krafft during
the Napoleonic wars, Sterrer
became involved with the
theme of soldiers' farewells
and returns during the First
World War. While the men
approach their insecure
destiny with motivation in
"Heimat – Aufruf" (1914–15),
the counterpart to *"Heimat –
Dein Mann"*, disability and
death (on the bottom left)
characterize their return. With
Sterrer, Krafft's Biedermeier
idyll becomes a strong
indictment.

Briefcase from the estate of Colonel Schneller and photograph of the Villa Giusti

Cover: substitute leather

The Villa Giusti (near Padua) was a guesthouse
for the Italian military leaders. On 3 November,
1918, the armistice between Austria-Hungary
and the allied and associated forces was signed
there. Colonel Karl Schneller, the Italian liaison
of the Austro-Hungarian Supreme Command,
took the contract to Vienna in this briefcase.

Garments and objects manufactured by Russian prisoners of war in Austria

*Russet jacket and peaked cap, plus dark brown trousers
made of paper*

These patterns were used to outfit the Russian prisoners
of war, whose uniforms had become unusable. Stringed
and plucked string instruments were also made of very
modest means.

Hall 7 | **Republic and Dictatorship**

Austria 1918–1945

Since the nationalities of Austria-Hungary had decided against a common empire after the First World War, the Germans of the Habsburg Monarchy also found it inevitable to form their own state. It was the victorious powers, however, who decided on the conditions on which this state should exist. The last Emperor, Charles I, went into exile. A possible union of Austria with Germany – an option which had been discussed for a considerable time – was prohibited by the Allies in the Peace Treaty of St Germain. For a while, the boundaries of the new state became the object of contention, especially the Southern border of Carinthia and the acquisition of the Burgenland. Establishing a solid economic foundation was also very difficult.

As the political powers in Austria mistrusted each other and as violence became a part of everyday politics, several rival paramilitary units came into existence; among those, the most significant were the *Heimwehr*, associated with the bourgeois camp; the *Republikanischer Schutzbund* ("Repu-

blican Guards") of the Social Democratic Party; the *Frontkämpfervereinigung* ("Union of the Front Fighters"); and the *Ostmärkische Sturmscharen* ("Storm Troopers of the *Ostmark*"). Finally, the paramilitary formations of the National Socialists developed. The total number of all paramilitary members sometimes exceeded the forces of the Federal Army several times.

Since 1927, Austria was in a state of civil war. The Austrian government became increasingly totalitarian: in 1933, it used a stalemate in the parliament as an excuse to dissolve parliament altogether, and, ultimately, the Constitution was also suspended. In February of 1934, with the insurgence of the *Schutzbund*, and, in July of 1934, with the assassination of Federal Chancellor Dollfuss by a National Socialist and extensive clashes in Vienna and several of the provinces, the civil war reached its climax. Austria became internationally isolated until Federal Chancellor Schuschnigg, after a meeting with Adolf Hitler, decided on a

Dr. Karl Renner

"A. D."

Oil on wood

State Chancellor 1918–1920 and
Federal President 1945–1950

Leopold Figl

THEODOR KLOTZ-DÜRRENBACH
(1890–1959)

Oil on canvas, 1955

Federal Chancellor 1945–1953

The proclamation of the Republic … in Vienna, 30 October, 1918

MAX FREY (1902–1955)

Oil on canvas

On 30 October, the provisional national assembly passed a resolution to found an independent state; on 12 November, the Republic of *Deutschösterreich* (German Austria) was proclaimed. The painter transposes the events both in time (30 October) and in place (to the Herrengasse). The crowd carries flags of both the German revolution and of the Bolshevists.

national poll concerning Austria's independence to be held on 13 March, 1938. Hitler reacted by ordering a military invasion of Austria and by the forced *Anschluss* (annexation) of Austria to the Third *Reich*.

In Austria, the Nazi dictatorship not only led to a change of the social elite, to enforced emigration and prosecution, but also, within a very short time, prepared the country for war. Soldiers from Austria participated in all military campaigns undertaken by the German Army, the *Wehrmacht*, and shared their destiny. Many Austrian soldiers were affected by the Battle of Stalingrad. On the other hand, Austrians also fought in the allied forces. Since 1943, the country, which was called the *"Alpen- und Donaureichsgaue"* (the Alpine and Danube *Reich* Districts), suffered from air raids and a partisan war that was conducted primarily from Yugoslavia. During this time, the prosecution of Jews and opponents to the Nazi regime also reached its peak. Despite the gradual development

of a resistance movement and the participation of Austrians in the attempt at assassinating Hitler on 20 July,1944, the country remained part of the political and military structure of the German *Reich*; from March to May 1945, it experienced war on its own territory and, finally, liberation through the allied forces and the capitulation of the German army. Soviet, American, British, and French troops occupied all of Austria. According to the final statistics, Austria, as part of the German *Reich*, had to provide around 1.2 million soldiers, of which a quarter million died or were reported missing; 65,000 Austrian Jews had been killed; the air raids and the action on Austrian soil made the total number of victims of the NS regime reach 380,000. By mid-April 1945, Dr. Karl Renner (1870–1950) managed to form a new Austrian government, to proclaim the country's independence and mark a new beginning.

Poster "Don't trust the enticing songs"

Design: ERNST KUTZER (1880–1965)

The poster refers to the referendum that was held in Ödenburg (Sopron) and its vicinity on 14 December, 1921, which promoted the inclusion of this area into the Republic of Austria. The cession of parts of German Western Hungary, as it was provided for in the Treaty of St Germain, was met with resistance. In an amendment to the peace treaty, a referendum was held in the Ödenburg district, which resulted in favor of Hungary.

Poster on the occasion of the Carinthian referendum on 10 October, 1920, advertising that the district should remain with Carinthia

The English translation of the Slovenian text reads: "Let us all vote! It is our sacred duty, our home country calls us. You are Carinthians and remain Carinthians!" The favourable attitude of the Slovenian-speaking Carinthians was one of the decisive factors that allowed the zone targeted by this referendum to remain with Austria.

Figure of a First Lieutenant of the German-Austrian *Volkswehr* 1918/20

Field-grey shirt, model 16, trousers, field-brown World War I steel helmet and pistol case made of tanned leather, with shoulder strap

The officers of the *Volkswehr* were only slightly different from those of the Austro-Hungarian army; the troops of the young republic could not afford new uniforms because of the economic crisis.

"Civil War"

Julius ENDLWEBER (1892–1947)

Oil on canvas, 1919

This painting depicts "Black Sunday", June 15, 1919, as radical leftists and communists tried to free their leaders who had been arrested the day before in the police prison in Vienna's Hörlgasse leading to the Votiv Church. Seventeen people were killed, as the crowd tried to break through a police barrier. Endlweber dramatizes the events by adding a flute-playing skeleton and a crucifix illuminated by light beams.

Figure of a member of the *Republikanischer Schutzbund* (left)

Brownish windcheater, loden knee-breeches, mountain boots, grey peaked cap with cockade and red carnation emblem

The *Schutzbund* had been established since 1923 and was deployed by the Social Democratic Party as a paramilitary formation. It assumed an important role in Austrian domestic politics and the civil war of 1934.

Battalion commander (rank of major) of the Upper Austrian *Heimwehr* (right)

Black-grey knee-breeches, brown-grey windcheater with black collar patches, insignia on the left sleeve, "Berndorf" steel helmet with wide green stripes as "Heimwehr" insignia.

The *Heimwehr* was anti-Marxist. In contrast to the Social Democrat *Schutzbund*, which was very uniform, there were many – sometimes also rival – subgroups in the *Heimwehr*. The *Heimwehr* also played an important role in the political clashes and the civil war of 1934.

Weapon used in the killings of Schattendorf

This hunting rifle, which was modified from an Austrian infantry weapon, belonged to a member of the *Frontkämpfervereinigung*. It was immediately confiscated by the police after the political unrest in Schattendorf on 30 January, 1927. During a march of the *Schutzbund*, one of the deadly shots was fired from this gun.

Figure of a *Generalmajor* of the Austrian federal army in dress uniform with field sash (1933–1938)

This uniform is almost identical with the field uniform for Imperial and Royal generals before 1918. Characteristic is the stiff high officer's cap; the stand-up collar with scarlet collar patches, golden braid trimmings, and a silver star of distinction; as well as a sash, worn around the hips, as military insignia.

Scorched documents from the palace of justice and *"Der Tag"* of 18 July, 1927

The persons accused of firing the deadly shots at Schattendorf were acquitted by a jury in July 1927. On 15 July, this caused a riot in Vienna: the palace of justice was set on fire. Police opened fire on the demonstrators, killing 90 people.

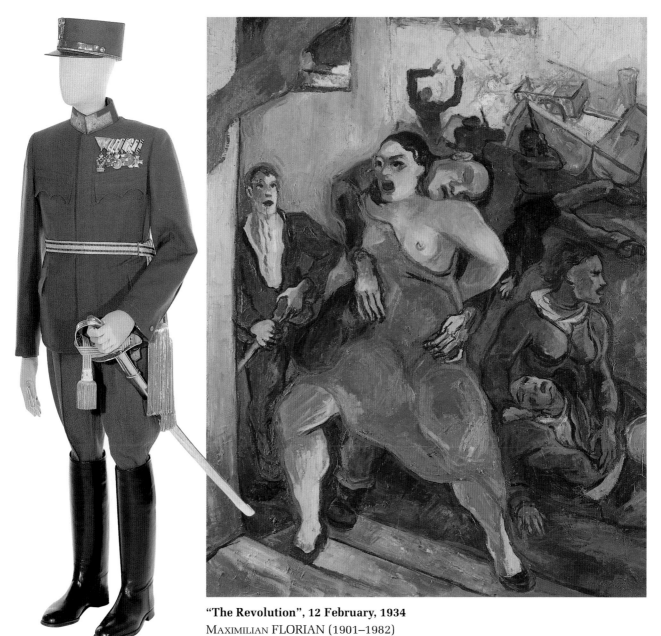

"The Revolution", 12 February, 1934

MAXIMILIAN FLORIAN (1901–1982)

Oil on canvas

In this important picture from the time between the wars, the painter captures the defence of the Engelshof at Herderplatz in Vienna-Simmering by the *Schutzbund* units in February 1934.

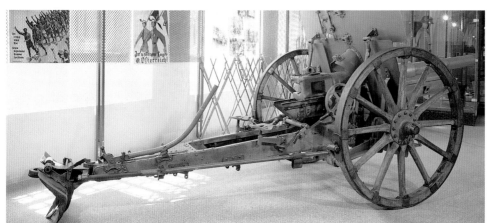

Field cannon, model of 1918

The 80-mm field cannon, developed during the last phase of the First World War, was used as standard artillery weapon by the Austrian federal army in the years between 1918 and 1938. During the civil war of 1934, weapons of this type were also used against the *Schutzbund*.

Dr. Engelbert Dollfuss

TOM VON DREGER (1868–1948)

Oil on plywood, 1934

Dr. Engelbert Dollfuss (1892–1934) was the Austrian Federal Chancellor from 1932 to 1934. On 1 May, 1934, he introduced the Constitution, making Austria a *Ständestaat* (corporate state). He was assassinated by the National Socialists on 25 July, 1934.

Dr. Kurt Schuschnigg

ANNA MAHLER (1904–1988)

Wooden plaster, bronzed, 1934

Dr. Kurt Schuschnigg (1897–1977) was the successor of Federal Chancellor Dollfuss. He could not prevent Austria's *Anschluss* by National Socialist Germany. He spent the war years in a concentration camp. Anna Mahler emigrated to Great Britain in 1938.

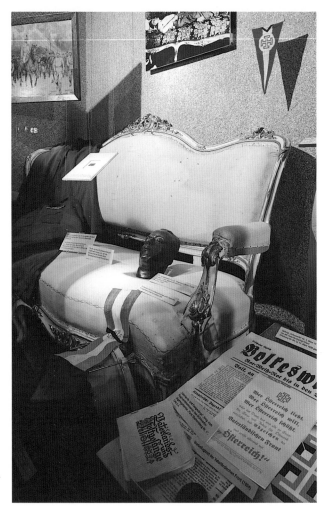

Bench from the office of Federal Chancellor Dollfuss

Seriously wounded during the storming of the Federal Chancellor's office, Dr. Dollfuss was laid on this bench; he died several hours later. The putschists had prohibited him from seeing either a doctor or a priest.

Fieseler Storch Aircraft

Since 1940, the Fi-156 C-3 *"Storch"* was used by the German *Wehrmacht* for reconnaissance and liaison purposes in particular. Because of the short runway needed for landing and taking off, this type of aeroplane could be used universally. The *Fieseler Storch* was deployed on all fronts in various models.

Nazi leaflets, some containing recommendations on how to vote for the referendum on 10 April, 1938

The referendum, which was held in the entire *Reich*, served as belated "legitimization" of the *Anschluss*, which had already taken place. As is usual in dictatorships, the referendum yielded the desired, almost unanimous result.

Officer's field blouse and field cap of the Austrian federal army, adapted for use in the German *Wehrmacht*

Officer's field blouse, model 33, with cavalry captains' ("Rittmeister") insignia of the German reconnaissance unit 11, with sewed-on stand-up collar made from navy-green fabric and braid trimmings, German sovereign eagle on the right breast pockets.

Field cap for other ranks, model 33, with insignia of the German artillery, woven cockade as a symbol of the Reich with right-angled piping in red colour, as well as woven-in national emblem

As there were not enough German uniforms after the integration of the Austrian federal army into the German *Wehrmacht*, Austrian uniforms were adapted.

The Guilty Bureaucrat

Alfred HRDLICKA (*1928)

Design for a memorial in Berlin (not executed), bronze, 1983

Together with architect Burkhard Grashorn, Hrdlicka participated in a contest. The meaning of the sculpture is evident: the guilty bureaucrat (SS-Obersturmbannführer Adolf Eichmann or someone else) is sitting before a pile of files, which later turns into the piles of human beings murdered during the Holocaust.

War remnants from the battlefield of Stalingrad

In November 1942, the 6th German army and parts of the 4th tank army, numbering around 250,000 men, were encircled in a basin of 50 by 30 km in the area of Stalingrad (today Volgograd). On 2 February, 1943, the remaining troops surrendered. Over 100,000 men were killed during this period, among them thousands of Austrians. 91,000 soldiers were taken prisoners by the Russians. Even today, remnants of this battle can be seen in the region around Volgograd.

Fanion of the First Austrian Volunteer Battalion

Cotton fabric in red-white-red, 1945

The flag was used by a battalion raised in 1944/45 by Austrian prisoners of war and resistance fighters. Since the battalion was established at a late point in time (in Riom, France, and Camp Suzzoni, North Africa), it could only be deployed for occupational purposes in Vorarlberg. The battalion was disbanded by the end of 1945.

Spherical one-man bunker from the *Reichsschutzstellung*

A large number of these combat and observation bunkers, which were produced by a simple concrete-casting technique, were used at the German-Hungarian border after September 1944. As later combat showed, however, the military advantage of these improvised bunkers was insignificant.

German demolition tank "Goliath"

The special vehicle 303 "Goliath" was a small, unmanned tank with an explosive charge of about 75 kg; it could be navigated, by remote control, to targets of up to 1000 m away, where it exploded with its charge. The "Goliath" was used during the Warsaw uprising (*"Warschauer Aufstand"*, August/September 1944) and during the Allied invasion in France (June 1944).

Figure of a member of the German *Volkssturm* 1944/45

Threadbare uniform of the German Wehrmacht and armband with the inscription "Deutscher Volkssturm/Wehrmacht". Weapon: Volkssturm carbine

The establishment of the German *Volkssturm* began in September 1944. The goal of this organization was to incorporate all males between the ages of 16 and 60. They were Nazi Germany's final effort. The gun consists of a crudely carved wooden shaft and adapted parts of the 98k carbine.

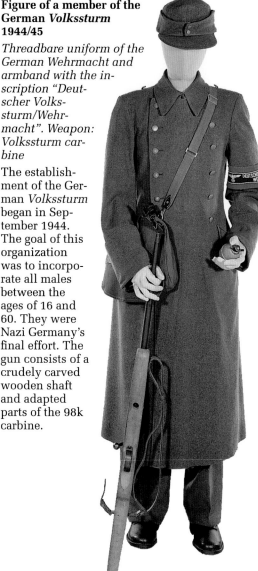

German 88-mm Flak 36

This cannon, which was used for air defence, was the standard German weapon during the Second World War and was employed until 1945. With the bomber units' increasing altitude, however, its range of 10,600 m was insufficient. On the ground, the Flak 36 was also used to defend against tanks.

Caterpillar "East"

The caterpillar "East" (prototype for use in mountainous areas shown here) was a development by the Steyr works. It transported art masterpieces from the *Kunsthistorisches Museum* (Museum of Art History) in Vienna, which had been designated for the so-called *Führermuseum*, into the mines of Altaussee.

Die Hitler-Armee hat den Krieg verloren

und nichts rettet sie mehr vor dem völligen Untergang. Unterstützt auf jede mögliche Weise die Truppen der Roten Armee bei der Zerschlagung und Vernichtung der Hitler-Truppen!

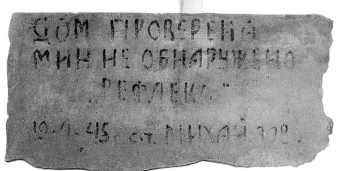

Russian signpost
Vienna 22 km

House inscription in Russian language

This inscription, which was taken from the house Brünnerstraße 76 in Vienna's 21st district, reads: "House checked, no mines found … 19.4.45…". By using stencils, such inscriptions were applied on several buildings in order to inform the following troops that the house had already been searched.

Figure of a U. S. bomber pilot in winter attire

Fur-lined uniform, aviation goggles, oxygen mask and life jacket

U. S. and British units conducted air raids against Austria between August 1943 and May 1945. The air raids reached their climax in the first months of 1945.

Pennants of the "Four in the Jeep"

During Austria's occupation, the patrolling vehicles used by the Viennese interallied commanders were recognizable by pennants of the allied forces.

Archduke Ferdinand Maximilian
GEORG DECKER (1819–1894)
Pastel on cardboard

Vice Admiral Wilhelm von Tegetthoff
GEORG DECKER (1819–1894)
Pastel on cardboard

Hall 8 | **Sea Power Austria**

The naval collection was not added to the permanent exhibition until after the Second World War. Since then, however, its has become one of the museum's most important parts, which tells of the former sea power of Austria.

Back in the 16th and 17th centuries, the Habsburg Monarchy already had warships at its disposal, but they primarily served for coastal defence or were used on the Danube. The River Troops achieved a considerable size. But only with the occupation of Venice as a result of the Peace Treaty of Campoformido (1797; formerly Campo Formio) did Austria gain an impressive navy. During the first half of the 19th century, its main port was Venice, but after converting Pola and Cattaro into major ports, they served as naval bases until the end of the Monarchy.

However, the awareness that the navy was a major source of power, developed very slowly. It was only the sea victories by Wilhelm von Tegetthoff near Helgoland (1864) and Lissa (1866) that made the navy's value evident. As a consequence, expanding the navy became especially important for the archdukes Ferdinand Max and Franz Ferdinand. By the First World War, the Austrian navy had finally become one of the biggest navies in the world.

The objects displayed in the exhibition explain how the Austrian navy negotiated its role between military requirements and attempted to be a valuable instrument of research for Europe and the world. Apart from magnificent figureheads and ship models – or the only preserved balloon-bombs of the *Uchatius* system that had been used during the siege of Venice in 1849 – this section contains mementoes of many navy commanders as well as depictions of Austria's presence at sea. The ships of the Austrian navy were also used for research excursions, training crew members, and showing "one's colours" on the seven seas. Thus, the model of the sail frigate *"Novara"* as well as drawings and watercolour paintings by Joseph Selleny recall the first circumnavigation of the globe by an Austrian war ship from 1857 to 1859. The initiator of this journey, Navy Commander Rear Admiral Archduke Ferdinand Maximilian, is remembered in

The Sea Battle of Lissa

CARL FREDERIK SØRENSEN (1818–1879)

Oil on canvas, 1868

This painting depicts the climax of the Sea Battle of Lissa on 20 July, 1866. The Austrian flag ship *"Erzherzog Ferdinand Max"* rammed the Italian armoured frigate *"Rè d'Italia"*, causing the ship to sink. The commander of the Austria naval unit, Rear Admiral Wilhelm von Tegetthoff, gained an unexpected victory during this second-largest sea battle of the 19th century.

pictures, uniform items, and other objects, as well as in various written records.

The Austro-Hungarian excursion to the North Pole from 1872 to 1874, which led to the discovery of the archipelago known as Franz Josef Land, was among the non-military endeavours of the navy.

Under the navy commanders Baron Hermann von Spaun, Count Rudolf Montecuccoli, and Anton Haus, the Austrian-Hungarian navy was modernized and prepared for war. Owing to the avid support of the successor to the throne, Franz Ferdinand, several new battleships were commissioned, and, since 1908, the first Austrian submarines were in use. Thus, at the beginning of the war, the Habsburg Monarchy was in charge of one of the most advanced navies in the world.

The special technical developments and, finally, the building of full-size warships before the First World War is illustrated by unique original objects and models. Among these, the sectional model of the last Austro-Hungarian flagship *"Viribus Unitis"* attains a special status. During the First World War, the Austro-Hungarian navy was primarily engaged with protecting the Dalmatian coast; the navy's strategic influence was limited to the Adriatic Sea due to the Allies' blockade at Otranto.

During the First World War, however, the heavily armoured warships played a less important role than the smaller units, especially the destroyers, the torpedo boats and submarines. Together with the aeroplanes patrolling the coast, they protected the coastal waters and the Adriatic Sea routes from the enemy.

The collapse of Austria-Hungary in the autumn of 1918 turned Austria into a landlocked country. The ships of the former navy were distributed among the victorious powers and the successor states. The end of the Austro-Hungarian navy is represented by the conning tower of the submarine U *"20"*, which sank in the northern Adriatic and was salvaged in 1962. Hardly anything survived of Austria's former sea power.

Model of a Danube frigate

Scale 1:24, 14 pairs of rudders, 2 breaker rudders, and 4 cannons under the foredeck

According to the assumption that ships successful at sea would also work on the Danube, vessels whose dimensions proved far too big were built in the 17th and 18th centuries. The Danube frigates, which had been built with considerable effort, could hardly manoeuvre on the Danube and repeatedly became stranded because the river was too shallow.

Model of Danube "monitors", type XI and XII

Scale 1:33, length 2.3 m

Since the American Civil War (1861–1865), monitors were built for battle on major rivers. The Austro-Hungarian navy soon owned the most modern flotilla of monitors in Europe. In 1916, the Danube monitors XI and XII were built as substitutes for the already outdated ships. Their building should have marked the final stage of the development of modern river battle ships. However, because of the shortage of raw material in 1917/18, not even the hulls could be finished.

Model of the frigate *"Novara"*

Scale 1:75

The *"Novara"* was built for the sea arsenal of Venice in 1850 and remodelled to a propeller-driven frigate in 1861/62. The *"Novara"* became famous for being the first Austrian ship to circumnavigate the globe, from 1857 to 1859. In 1867, the frigate transported home the body of Emperor Maximilian of Austria, who had been shot in Mexico.

Human types

JOSEF SELLENY (1824–1875)

Pencil drawing with water colours

Landscape painter Josef Selleny participated in the *"Novara's"* circumnavigation of the globe from 1857 to 1859; his numerous water colour paintings accurately document the individual stages of the journey. His interests included coastal and island landscapes, but basically focused on the depiction of people.

Figure of an Austro-Hungarian sailor in summer uniform

Commander's Cross of the Order of Maria Theresa

Gold, enamel

For his victory against the Italian fleet at the Sea Battle of Lissa, Vice Admiral Wilhelm von Tegetthoff (1827–1871) was promoted commander of Austria's most prestigious military award. Numerous other honours were to follow.

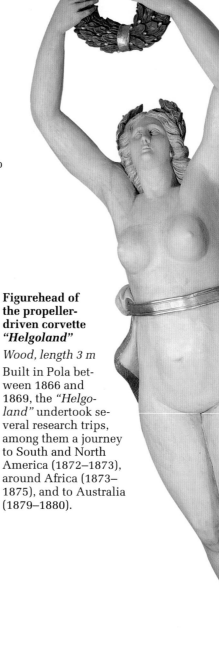

Figurehead of the propeller-driven corvette *"Helgoland"*

Wood, length 3 m

Built in Pola between 1866 and 1869, the *"Helgoland"* undertook several research trips, among them a journey to South and North America (1872–1873), around Africa (1873–1875), and to Australia (1879–1880).

Honorary present from the city of Trieste for Vice Admiral Wilhelm von Tegetthoff

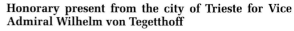

MAYERHOFER AND KLINKOSCH, court goldsmith's studio, Vienna (design by Völker)

Silver, gold-plated, 1867

Trieste's importance as a seaport and a centre of commerce is symbolized by the allegorical figures of shipbuilding, navigation, commerce, and industry. The triton at the top of the sculpture is lifting the armoured frigate *"Erzherzog Ferdinand Max"*, Tegetthoff's flagship.

"There can be no going back!"

JULIUS VON PAYER (1841–1915)

Oil on canvas, 1892

The discovery of Franz Josef Land (at 80 degrees northern latitude) was the main scientific event of the Austro-Hungarian expedition to the North Pole from 1872 to 1874. Julius Payer, one of the two leaders of the expedition, later captured his impressions in several paintings. This painting depicts the moment when the ship's commander, *Linienschiffsleutnant* Carl Weyprecht, convinces the crew to continue their march south after they had left the ship ("There can be no going back!").

Julius von Payer and his note scroll "The Serpent"

A few years before his death, the once celebrated and later isolated Julius Ritter von Payer (1841–1915), recorded his reflections on his life and his times on various pieces of paper. They were glued together and called "The Serpent" by Payer. In this manner, 24 scrolls were produced.

Dress coat of the Austro-Hungarian Admiral Count Montecuccoli

Navy-blue fabric, open cut, gold buttons with anchor emblem and the imperial crown. Admiral's insignia at the end of the sleeves. On the top braid trimming, the so-called "Elliot's eye" for combatants

As navy commander and head of the navy section in the ministry of war, Count Rudolf Montecuccoli (1843–1922) was largely responsible for modernizing the Austro-Hungarian navy.

Sectional model of the battleship *"Viribus Unitis"*

Scale 1:25, length about 6 m

"Viribus Unitis" was the last flagship of the Austro-Hungarian navy; together with three sister ships, she was part of the nucleus of the battleship fleet during the First World War. On 31 October, 1918, the ship was sunk a few hours after its surrender to Yugoslavia on the occasion of an Italian command operation. This model was built for the Technical Museum in Vienna by eight skilled workers in the Stabilimento Tecnico Triestino shipyard between 1913 and 1917. The ship's design, the floor plan, and the machine installation are identical with the original.

Spoils and photographs of the suppression of the Boxer Rebellion in China, 1900

Members of the Austro-Hungarian army were involved in the suppression of the Boxer Rebellion as part of an international intervention. The photos show sailors from the *"Aspern"* on a customary local vehicle; Taku-Forts after being captured; Beijing, 20 August, 1900: the gate in the wall is set on fire.

Glasses with navy emblems

Company J. & L. Lobmeyr, Vienna

Thin crystal glass, engraved, with anchor emblem, ca. 1900

Glasses of this kind were made for the navy officers' messes and clubs.

Whitehead torpedo

Length 3.35 m, diameter 350 mm

This torpedo was developed by Robert Whitehead in collaboration with the Austrian frigate captain Johann Luppis. It is considered the first functional torpedo in naval history and was adopted by most navies.

Conning tower and pressure hull fragment of the submarine U "20"

In mid-1918, this submarine, which was finished in 1917, was attacked and sunk by an Italian submarine near the mouth of the Tagliamento river in the northern Adriatic. The tower and parts of the pressure hull were salvaged in 1962.

Grand Admiral Anton Haus

MIKLOS LIGETI (1871–1944)

White marble, 1916

Anton Haus (1851–1917) was Commander of the Austro-Hungarian Imperial and Royal fleet at the outbreak of the First World War. Despite the pronounced superiority of Austria-Hungary's enemies, he was successful in defending its coasts and harbours. Haus, who is here depicted one year before his death, died on board of his flagship *"Viribus Unitis"* on 8 February, 1917.

***Linienschiffsleutnant* Baron Gottfried von Banfield and his air fighter pilots**

KARL STERRER (1885–1972)

Blending technique on paper, 1918

The picture shows the commander of the coastal airport of Trieste, Baron von Banfield (1890–1986), with two air pilots, who died in battle soon afterwards. Banfield was one of Austria-Hungary's most successful naval air pilots and was a Knight of the Order of Maria Theresa.

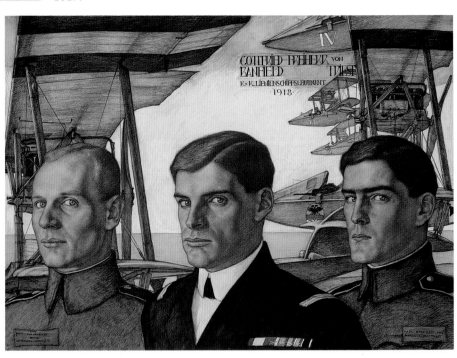

Artillery Halls

The artillery collection in the Museum of Military History comprises about 550 pieces of artillery and ordnance. It is thus considered one of the most important collections of its kind. Most of the stock is from the old imperial arsenal. By integrating prototypes and experimental artillery, the collection kept growing and was complemented with various new additions during the First World War. The overall number of all artillery weapons can only be estimated today; it is around 1,200. During the Second World War, several historically valuable objects were melted down and used for producing iron and other non-ferrous metals. This process was continued during the immediate post-war period in order to finance the reconstruction of the museum through sale of the melted gun material.

Besides the objects that are exhibited in the halls or in front of the museum, the majority is housed in two extra buildings (objects 2 and 17), the so-called "artillery halls".

The building that can be seen to the left of the museum shows how Austrian artillery developed from the Middle Ages to the 18th century. In a small side-room, the historically most valuable treasures, the wrought-iron cannons from the middle ages, can be seen. Next to smaller stone-mortars from the 15th century, the "Pumhart von Steyr", a stone-mortar of a thousand pounds, is most impressive. The other room as well as the middle area of the building is dedicated to bronze cannons from the 16th, 17th, and 18th centuries.

The right artillery hall mainly comprises the stock of "foreign" artillery, which is exhibited in the middle area. Apart from Venetian and Turkish cannons, there are several French examples, mostly spoils from the wars between 1792 and 1813. Both side rooms again house pieces of Austrian artillery. In one room, several breech-loaders can be seen, in the other, objects that illustrate the transition to modern artillery between the 19th and 20th centuries.

Thousand-pound stone-mortar

Wrought-iron, total length 2555 mm, length of the barrel 1244 mm, calibre 882 mm, weight 7,100 kg

This thousand-pound giant stone-mortar bears the name of *"Pumhart von Steyr"* and is considered to be one of the oldest cannons in the world. It was made during the first half of the 15th century and is an example of the so-called *Stabringtechnik*, a special technique using iron rods and rings that came into use in the production of gunnery in the late Middle Ages. The range of this mortar was about 600 m.

The *"Nürnberger Monatsrohre"* (Nuremberg culverins of the months)

Bronze, calibre 78 mm

This collection consists of twelve three-pound culverins that were cast by JOHANN BALTHASAR HEROLD in Nuremberg in 1708. The embellishments on each cannon refer to a specific month of the year; thus, the cannons served more representative than military purposes.

Half-size cannon royal called *"Singerin"*

Recoil base with handle in the form of a "wild man"

The classification of the cannon as a "singer" is reflected on the barrel: the chase of the gun bears the picture of a singing bird.

24-pound battery cannon, model of 1861

Cast iron, calibre 150 mm

Cannons of this kind were the first breech-loaders to be introduced into the Austrian army. The *Wahrendorf*-system lock and the rifled barrel guaranteed rapid firing and remarkable accuracy. Although antiquated, cannons of this system were still used during the First World War.

Austrian artillery in front of the museum building

Tank Collection

The first armoured vehicles were already used in Europe around the turn of the century. Usually, these were civilian vehicles fortified with armour-plates and equipped with machine guns. In Austria-Hungary, Colonel Burstyn, in 1911, designed a new model different from these earlier types. It was no longer driven by traditional wheels, but by tracks. However, because of technical and financial problems, this project was never put into practice.

The idea of tracked armoured battle vehicles experienced a temporary climax during the First World War. In the time between the wars, the Austrian federal army had armoured vehicles of predominantly Italian make. During the Second World War, faster, armoured units became the basic requirement for a new form of combat, the so-called *"Blitzkrieg"*, which was to characterize the first phase of this war.

In the so-called "tank garden" behind the museum building, the most important combat vehicles of the Austrian Armed Forces after 1955 are exhibited. The different types vividly exemplify the continual development of armour plating techniques. The first Austrian armoured units after 1955 were mainly equipped with vehicles from the allied forces. For the most part, they date back to the Second World War, as, for example, the US armoured scout car, model 8, the armoured personnel carrier, model 21, or the light battle tank, model 24. Among Soviet battle vehicles, the most important standard models, the battle tank 34/85 and the self-propelled gun SU 100, are on display. The latter had originally been put up in front of the liberation memorial of the Red Army on Schwarzenbergplatz. The newer battle vehicles are of U. S., British, and French origin. Only a few types of the vehicles on display are from Austria, although the prototype of an armoured personnel carrier (which, however, never made it into production) and the light tank *"Kürassier"* (model "Super-K"), a variant based on the French AMX 13 , deserve special mention.